COMMUNITY, PROFESSIONS AND BUSINESS

Community, Professions and Business:

A history of the Central Manchester Teaching Hospitals and the National Health Service

Helen K. Valier and John V. Pickstone

Community, Professions and Business: a history of the Central Manchester Teaching Hospitals and the National Health Service

Copyright © Helen K. Valier and John V. Pickstone, 2008

Published by Central Manchester and Manchester Children's University Hospital NHS Trust, in association with the Centre for the History of Science, Technology and Medicine, University of Manchester

Distributed by Carnegie Publishing, 01524 840111
www.carnegiepublishing.com

ISBN 13: 978-0-9558971-2-2

Designed and Typeset by Carnegie Book Production, Lancaster
Printed and bound by Information Press, Oxford

In memory of
Edward Pickstone
(1908–1967)

And in recognition of all who have served
the hospitals here described

Contents

Preface and Acknowledgements

IN DECEMBER 2001 the Central Manchester and Manchester Children's University Hospital NHS Trust wanted to commission a book to mark the 250th anniversary of the Manchester Infirmary's foundation in 1752. Updating the history written by William Brockbank, *A Portrait of a Hospital, 1752–1948: To Commemorate the Bicentenary of the Royal Infirmary*, was an obvious choice, and they approached John Pickstone at the Wellcome Unit and Centre for the History of Science, Technology & Medicine (CHSTM) at the University of Manchester. CHSTM were happy to be involved, and Frances Dawbarn was initially engaged for the project, providing early groundwork and interviews. Helen Valier did most of the new research and, together with John Pickstone, wrote and revised the manuscript. The Trust provided the major funding for this project, and the CHSTM contributed additional resources.

Until 1948, the Infirmary had been a stand–alone teaching and charity institution, serving the poor of the City while providing for the education of young doctors. With the coming of the new National Health Service, the Infirmary became linked to its neighbouring hospitals and to national government. Our history focuses on the central Manchester teaching hospitals to show how the NHS operated at a local level and how local developments interacted with national policy. Because the Trust now includes the children's hospitals we have included them in the history, both for our overview of the period before 1948, and (briefly) for their subsequent history.

We are extremely grateful to all those who assisted our efforts, including Michael Worboys and our other colleagues at CHSTM. The librarians at the Central Trust and the University have been generous with time and resources, as have the many current and former employees whom we interviewed and from whom we solicited advice. We are particularly grateful to Christine Hallett, Derek Welsh and Joan Higgins for commenting on the manuscript, although editorial responsibilities rest solely with the authors. Derek has been a constant support, even when the pressures of rebuilding the hospitals substantially delayed the arrival of the history. The photographs are from the Medical Illustrations Department of the Central Trust, and we are grateful to Brian Williams and Greg Harding for their help, as well as Brian Chapman of LIMEart. All photographs are reproduced with the kind permission of the Trust. We also are grateful for the help of Carnegie Publishers, and especially Anna Hodge.

Helen Valier extends her thanks to Julie Anderson, Hilde and Mike Ettrick, and Roberta Bivins for their help and support during the writing of the book. Both authors are grateful to Joanna Baines for her close reading during the final stages. John Pickstone thanks all those who should have seen more of him.

There was much more that could have been included in this history; much has been left out or only partially told. In this regard we ask the forgiveness of our informants and the patience of our readers. Histories of hospitals within the NHS remain few – much more needs to be written about what has happened since 1948, and especially in the recent, turbulent decades.

As this book goes to press, the Central Manchester Hospitals are part of a massive rebuilding scheme, and of an expanded NHS Trust seeking Foundation status. We hope our history will inform and encourage all those who make that future.

HKV & JVP, July 2008

Helen K. Valier now teaches in the Honors College at the University of Houston, Texas. John V. Pickstone is Wellcome Research Professor in the Centre for the History of Science, Technology and Medicine at the University of Manchester.

CHAPTER ONE

The Hospitals
of Central Manchester

M OST OF THIS BOOK focuses on the history of the Manchester
Royal Infirmary and its associated hospitals for the sixty years
after the Second World War. When this main account starts, the
MRI had existed for almost two centuries as an independent charity
hospital, but that phase of its life ended in 1948, under the new
National Health Service, when the MRI was officially joined with
the neighbouring hospitals which also served as teaching hospitals
for the medical school of the University of Manchester. With St.
Mary's Hospital for Women and Children, the Manchester Royal Eye
Hospital, the Dental Hospital and the Manchester Foot Hospital, the
MRI formed the United Manchester Hospitals. So they continued
to 1974. How they developed, and what happened after 1974, you
can read below.

In 2001, the collaboration was extended. The Trust then running
the University Hospitals of Central Manchester was expanded
to include the local children's hospitals – the Royal Manchester
Children's Hospital at Pendlebury and the Booth Hall Children's
Hospital in north Manchester. It is now intended to move children's
services to the central Manchester site, thus forming one of the
largest hospital complexes in Britain. So children's hospitals are also
part of our story.

Our book was commissioned to celebrate 250 years of the MRI
(1752–2002), but it is also a contribution to the Trust that now unites
six of the major medical institutions of the conurbation. In this
introductory chapter we will explore how all these hospitals were
created and changed, and how they were related to each other before
the National Health Service. In the main chapters of the book we
focus on the MRI and the other central hospitals, and at the end
we return to the wider view of the complex of hospitals which will
now go forward together.

Of the six hospitals now linked, five were once independent hospital charities – voluntary hospitals as they were called. The exception is Booth Hall, which was built in north Manchester to be the 'workhouse infirmary' for the Poor Law Guardians of Prestwich – the statutory body responsible for the support of the destitute in that district. When it opened in 1906, Booth Hall was a smaller version of the Withington Infirmary then run by the South Manchester Guardians, or the Crumpsall Infirmary, run by the Manchester Guardians and also in north Manchester. Booth Hall was used as a military hospital at the start of the Great War, but in 1915 these three Boards of Guardians, which together covered Manchester, were merged. It was then decided to use Booth Hall as a children's hospital for the destitute of the whole city. In terms of beds, it was the largest children's hospital in England, and almost unique in being run by the Poor Law.

Whilst Booth Hall served the children of the very poor and was paid for 'on the rates', the other five hospitals were paid for by donations and legacies, and increasingly by regular small payments from working people. These voluntary hospitals had been founded at different times and with different relations to the medical profession, so between them our hospitals speak of many strands in the history of medicine and the history of Manchester.

The MRI was begun in 1752 as the first and central medical charity of a growing city. St. Mary's was created in 1790, when some powerful surgeons and 'men-midwives' broke away from the Infirmary and founded a 'Lying-in Charity' to attend poor women in child-birth. The Eye Hospital and the Children's Hospital were started in the early nineteenth century as small charities, mostly dealing with outpatients. They were evidence of doctors seeking careers through specialization, or wanting to attend to patients who were excluded from the general hospitals. The dental hospital was founded in 1884 to serve the dental school by allowing staff and students to attend to patients unable to pay for private dental treatment. All these hospitals were intended for the poor; it was not until the end of the nineteenth century that richer folk sought hospital treatment.

The chief medical charity of Manchester

In the mid eighteenth century, hospitals were a new fashion. In the chief towns of the counties of England, gentlemen and doctors with plans for hospitals sought the support of aristocrats and of the town's people. Manchester was not officially the capital of Lancashire, but it was the focus of manufacturing, as Liverpool was the thriving port. Liverpool had launched an Infirmary in 1746 and Manchester followed suit in 1752, stimulated by a young surgeon, Charles White, who had recently returned after training in London with William Hunter, a leading physician and exponent of obstetrics. White was to remain the Infirmary's leading doctor until he led the secession of 1790.

In 1755, after three years in a rented house, the Infirmary committee built a monumental building in Piccadilly, then on the edge of town. It was served by three physicians and three surgeons, who gave their services as part of the charity. This was not unmixed philanthropy, however, for if the subscribers elected you to such a post they attested your quality and aided your private practice. Surgeons also gained money by taking apprentices, for which a hospital attachment was a considerable advantage. That senior doctors gave honorary service as an adjunct to private practice remained the pattern for voluntary hospitals until the NHS, though by then some payments had been introduced, and some private patients were being admitted to charity hospitals where they paid for their doctoring.

As well as admitting 'in-patients' to the wards, the early Infirmary also saw outpatients, and its staff made visits to the homes of patients, especially those with the fever (mainly that later known as typhus) which was characteristic of crowded and dirty accommodation. In any case, patients or their carers had to seek recommendation tickets from the richer people who subscribed to the Infirmary funds. Afterwards, they were supposed to give thanks – to their subscribers, and sometimes by placing a note of gratitude in the local church.

Manchester's Infirmary, as the chief charity of a thriving town, proved remarkably successful, and then remarkably controversial. By the 1780s, it had a created a satellite hospital for lunatics, which remained in Piccadilly until the 1840s. By then it was in the centre of a dense and dirty conurbation, whilst the new County lunatic asylums, provided on the rates, were out of town. The Lunatic Hospital also too sought the healthful countryside, and it remains today as Cheadle Royal – a private mental hospital mostly funded from the NHS.

The Infirmary also built a suite of baths, mainly so the subscribers could enjoy a healthy immersion without journeying to the spa at Buxton. At the end of the 1780s, it also planned a new building for its outpatient clinic, and a doubling of the honorary medical and surgical staff. The expansion was promoted by the town's reformers and political radicals, and opposed by Charles White and his fellow surgeons who were mostly Tories and Anglicans. As the country argued over responses to the French Revolution, over slavery, and over the rights of protestant dissenters outside the Church of

England, Manchester also debated the future of its Infirmary. The reformers won, and soon added a fever hospital – the first in Britain. White and his surgical friends resigned and founded a new charity, to provide midwives and doctors for poor mothers in childbirth; this became St. Mary's.

Midwifery had traditionally been an occupation for women; doctors were only called in emergencies, often to remove a dead foetus. But around the mid eighteenth century, it had become fashionable to engage a suitable physician or surgeon to attend normal deliveries. Some of these 'men-midwives' founded charity hospitals for obstetrics, but these ventures proved much less popular than the new general hospitals, mainly because of high rates of infection among the babies and the mothers. The Manchester Charity for Lying-in Women, founded by Charles White, took a small house for a few inpatients, and then moved in 1795 to a larger building, also in Salford; but it was chiefly a domiciliary service, and entirely so from 1815 to 1850.

Promoting births had been a popular cause in the mid 1700s, when an increase of population seemed important for the power of a country, but by the 1820s (and for about 70 years thereafter) the population problem was reversed. Industrial Britain seemed to have far too many people – hence the rising cost of maintaining paupers on the Poor Law rates, and hence too a suspicion of any charities which might seem to encourage births among the poor. Many middle-class women, however, sympathized with poor mothers and thought the Lying-in Charity worth supporting. And in spite of the poverty of the new industrial city, with its sewage-sodden yards and damp cellars, the charity's death rates for domiciliary deliveries compared very well with those for private medical practice among the well to do.

Generally, however, and especially for the infants and for children, Manchester's death rates were enormous. From about 1825 to about 1850, the doctors employed by medical charities were key witnesses to the conditions of the poor. They went where few of their social class ventured; they helped build a body of social reportage which made Manchester the shock city of the age and fed into the campaigns for sanitation, and helped produce the first Public Health Act in 1848

Not only the poor felt crowded. From the 1810s, as surgeons returned from the wars with France, and as private medical schools boomed, many urban doctors felt the pressure of competition. The deference given to physicians and to some surgeons in the previous century had faded in the dense new cities. Starting your own hospital was a good way to advertise, and specializing in eyes was an early way to create a niche; a surgeon skilled in the treatment of eye injuries, the removal of cataracts or the correction of squints could attract a good clientele. The first eye hospital had been founded in London in 1805; William James Wilson trained there and in 1814 opened a similar institution in Manchester after encouraging a group of gentlemen to give financial support. The Infirmary was not pleased because of the implication that their own eye surgery was not adequate, so Wilson made his early links with the rival Lying-In Charity. But by 1827, he had made his name and was elected to the Infirmary staff as a full surgeon.

The Manchester Eye Hospital continued with new doctors; Thomas Windsor, one of the nation's best-known oculists, served there for 10 years. Over the next decades it moved house several times, and experienced several quarrels between its doctors and its lay governors. Such disagreements were then common in voluntary hospitals – doctors were highly competitive and some of them saw the charities as extensions of their own practices, while some business-men governors treated the doctors as employees rather than members of a liberal profession.

Many other small medical charities were founded between 1810 and 1850, usually as 'Dispensaries' treating outpatients and home patients rather than admitting inpatients. Some served particular districts, such as the Dispensaries in Ancoats and Salford (which later became full hospitals), while others served patients who were excluded from general hospitals – like the Lock Hospital for women with venereal disease. Children were not admitted to general hospitals and for them two general practitioners, John Alexander and W. Barton Stott, established a Dispensary in 1829. Both doctors served for many years, treating about 1500 children a year as outpatients or by visiting their homes.

All these smaller charities struggled in the 1830s and '40s, especially during the severe economic depressions when charity money was short and disease thrived in the general poverty. Many businessmen were then suspicious of charity as undermining self-reliance, but support improved in the 1850s. From the 1860s, when standards of living began to rise, the suspicion of charity diminished and 'civic pride' extended. By the 1870s, the workers themselves could contribute to hospital collections.

Early Victorian moves

Much of the Infirmary was re-constructed around 1850, funded partly by the sale of the fever hospital whose site had increased in value when Portland Street was developed as a major thoroughfare. The Lunatic Asylum, as we noted, had moved to Cheadle, and the Public Baths had been discontinued. Indeed, the governors considered and rejected a plan to move the whole institution out of the city centre and build larger where land was cheaper. Instead, they converted their eighteenth century sprawl of buildings into a compact civic monument at the heart of the sooty city. The Infirmary was famous for its industrial accident cases: tourists who came to see the factories and warehouses would also call at the Infirmary to see industry's victims. As an iconic monument it ranked with the new Town Hall built in the 1820s on Cross Street (on the site of Charles White's town house; and replaced by the Albert Square building in the mid 1870s).

The rebuilding of the Infirmary did not, however, create many extra beds, once allowance was made for the fever patients now to be accommodated in the main building. The Infirmary was a teaching hospital, linked with the proprietary medical schools run by doctors in the neighbouring streets, but it did not impress those local doctors who were interested in public health. It was their society, the Manchester and Salford Sanitary Association, which pushed the Infirmary to adopt the new form of nursing which Florence Nightingale was developing at St Thomas' in London. It was one of Nightingale's local allies, the St. Mary's surgeon John Roberton, who from the 1850s led the criticism of the Infirmary building as unhealthy. This sanitary critique was repeated in the 1860s and 1870s, and it fed into the complex, long-running dispute as to whether the hospital should move out of town. One partial solution was a rural convalescent home: the Infirmary's branch at Cheadle, south of the city, was given by Robert Barnes in the mid 1860s, so that patients could recover in the country air.

The Lying-In Hospital had suffered a fire in 1847, and for some time it shared the premises of the Eye Hospital next door in South Parade. It was led by an energetic senior medical officer, Thomas Radford, whose wife was good at mobilizing the middle-class ladies who were increasingly prominent in the public life of the city. Attitudes to charity were softer where the beneficiaries were women and children, and the Radfords managed to fund a new building on Quay Street. They renamed the charity as 'the St. Mary's Hospital and Dispensary for the Diseases peculiar to Women and also for the Diseases of Children'. They planned about 60 beds for women and 20–30 for children, and the outpatient service was developed as the hospital tried to shift its emphasis away from maternity and towards gynaecology. One of the new surgeons, Charles Clay, was already famous for the removal of ovarian cysts – a heroic form of surgery pioneered in Ashton-under-Lyne (and the American Midwest). The next major St. Mary's doctor was Lloyd Roberts, who made a fortune as one of the country's best-known gynaecologists.

That St. Mary's sought to include children may owe something to developments at the Children's Dispensary, which had survived for 20 years as a minor charity but was then being re-energized by an immigrant doctor. After the 1848 Revolution failed in Germany, several radical European doctors came to or through Manchester. Abraham Jacobi, for example, came here to see Friedrich Engels, the friend and supporter of Karl Marx; Engels did not think Jacobi had the disposition to succeed in medicine, and was rather glad when he left for the USA –where he became known as 'the father of American paediatrics'. A Hungarian doctor, Augustus Merei, again with an interest in children, was settled in Manchester by 1850. With James Whitehead of St. Mary's, he started a Clinical Hospital for the Diseases of Children, in Stevenson Square. It functioned as a Dispensary and was closely connected with public health work. In 1867, it moved to Cheetham Hill as a 20 bed hospital – later the Northern Hospital.

The community of German merchants in Manchester was crucial for these developments, and not least for Dr Louis Borchardt, who moved here in 1853 and was soon appointed as physician to the General Dispensary for Children. In 1856–7, as Merei was setting up in Stevenson Square, Borchardt opened a six-bed hospital in St. Mary's Parade, near the premises which the Lying-In Hospital was about to vacate. Borchardt stressed learning and research – in which German doctors were often in advance of the British, and he also stressed the importance of child health for the future labour force. That mortality was so high among children had become a theme of the sanitary movement; children's hospitals could be expected to reduce the death rates especially for infectious diseases.

In 1859, when St. Mary's was having trouble paying for their new building, they invited the Children's Hospital to merge with them; but Borchardt was not keen, and in 1860 the children's hospital moved to new premises in Bridge Street, with 25 beds. There it stayed until 1873, when they moved out of town and built a new hospital in Pendlebury, where the patients could benefit from lots of fresh air. Because this site was too remote for parents to attend easily, the charity also maintained a central dispensary in Gartside Street for outpatients.

By 1880, the Pendlebury hospital exemplified much that was then new about hospitals. Its building for 140 beds was in the pavilion (Nightingale) style which allowed ventilation by means of windows along each side of the long wards. It incorporated wards for infectious diseases, as part of the city's response to the high death rates of urban children (another part was the Monsall isolation hospital, which, like the Infirmary's convalescent hospital was given by Robert Barnes and initially run as a branch of the Infirmary). The nursing at Pendlebury was superintended by a 'Nightingale nurse' who brought social and professional authority to a role that had been seen as only domestic management. Sometimes this new breed of matrons clashed with doctors who were not used to sharing authority; sometimes they were idolized, as with Grace Campbell at Pendlebury who came from a wealthy, military, but radical Scottish family, and who served as Nurse Superintendent from 1877 to 1879 – when she married a doctor.

She left at about the same time as Dr Borchardt retired. He was succeeded by Henry Ashby, who was London-trained and had served briefly as a children's physician and lecturer at Liverpool medical school. Ashby became a world authority on paediatrics, including nurseries and school health, at a time when the study of children became a focus for several nascent academic disciplines. For many years he worked with George Wright, a pioneer of surgery in children as the scope of (aseptic) surgery expanded rapidly at the end of the century. By the beginning of the twentieth century, industrial and imperial competition between nations had made 'national efficiency' a national slogan, and infant mortality a national scandal. When the country was said to need more and healthier babies, then national and local funds were made available for clinics and for midwives. From 1900 until the Second World War, this 'populationist' concern with the health of mothers, children and workers was a major driver of governmental expenditure.

Big business and the teaching hospital

Around the same time as the children's hospital moved out to Pendlebury, Manchester's new College moved to Rusholme, then a residential suburb. Owens College too had a fine new building, in the Gothic style then in vogue for academic buildings. The College had been founded in 1851 when John Owens, a local business-man without children, left his fortune to establish an institution which would teach much the same subjects as in Oxford and Cambridge, but without the religious restrictions; Owens College would be open to (male) students of all faiths or none. It began in the house on Quay Street that had belonged to Richard Cobden, the mill owner who had led the national campaign for free trade, and it almost failed. Initially, few fathers saw the benefit of giving a liberal education to sons who were intended for business.

By the 1860s, however, higher education, like charity, was becoming more popular. The growth of London University as a national examining body for degrees had encouraged the beginnings of 'diploma culture', and Owens had changed its image by stressing the sciences, especially chemistry. Henry Roscoe, its new professor of chemistry, was well connected to local industrialists and he preached the advantages of German University education for would-be professionals. But his claim went much wider: laboratory science epitomized the spirit of free enquiry; it was the source of knowledge on which material progress depended; training in research fitted a man for any career which needed initiative, judgment and tenacity.

These same attitudes were needed in medicine. That, at least, was the opinion of the professors who agreed to include the local medical school in the plans for development in Rusholme. This merger with Owens had been considered in 1856, after the two local medical schools had combined their forces; but medical students then had a reputation as rude and rowdy, as unlikely to linger over self-development, and liable to lower the tone of a liberal arts college. Fifteen years later, however, the image of medical students had been raised a little, partly by evangelical teachers aiming to create Christian gentlemen. Medical teachers were now pressing for increased educational standards – for higher entry qualifications and for more science in the courses. By merging with Owens, the medical teachers in Manchester would lose some of their previous independence, but most of them would come to enjoy increased status as the medical faculty of a college intent on recognition as a university. The students would gain from a broader staff and increased facilities; and Owens College, like the Scottish Universities and the university colleges in London, would be able to rely on the medical fees. A new medical school was built behind the main college buildings, and was opened in 1873 by T. H. Huxley – a friend of Roscoe, a champion of Darwinism, and the national leader in the promotion of science.

But what would be the relation of the new suburban medical school to the Infirmary in Piccadilly? In 1876, after the Infirmary was again criticized as unsanitary and too small, several leading trustees proposed that the value of the central site should be realized by moving out. To retain easy access for emergency cases fifty beds would be housed in a new central building, but a new 400-bed hospital would be built in Rusholme. At a special meeting, however, the plan was defeated by 115 votes to 104. The opposition, which included some leading doctors, wished to ensure that the Infirmary remained a central civic institution, under the eye of a 'large and intelligent body of Trustees'. They saw the Infirmary as increasingly dominated by its doctors and by a small but powerful business-elite who were also the backers of Owens College. This elite, of course, saw themselves as friends of progress, science and good management

– as helping the professors create a centre for medical education and modern practice which could rival anything in the nation. Science was credited with transforming medicine: anaesthetics had encouraged the expansion of surgery and germ theories of disease now promised better prevention and therapies, including antiseptic surgery.

The modernizers won, but it took them twenty-five years. They owed their eventual victory to a new form of power – to large legacies left for charity in care of a few influential trustees. In Manchester, the largest of these new trusts was the £300,000 left by Joseph Whitworth, a local engineer internationally famous for his techniques of standardization and for arms manufacture. The Whitworth trustees were keen supporters of Owens, where one of them, R. D. Christie, had been professor of law and history. They offered to buy land just to the south of the new College and to build a hospital for teaching, with special facilities for skin diseases and cancer. It was intended to supplement the Infirmary, but the Infirmary trustees opposed the plan and suggested instead an extension on the Piccadilly site. The executors responded by buying the 'Owens College Estate' as a resource for the college, on which it might provide teaching hospitals. The college then offered a site for the rebuilding of the whole Infirmary, but this was refused, as was the renewed suggestion of an Infirmary extension in Rusholme.

Not until 1902 did the Infirmary decide to move. By then the College had become an independent University offering its own medical degrees; by then the old Infirmary seemed even more out of date, and the City Council wanted the Piccadilly site for more tram stops and for an art gallery (which was never built). Sixty years after the first discussion of a move, the Infirmary opened its new, pavilion building in 1908. For the first time, it had an X-ray department, albeit in the basement along with electrotherapeutics. The old hospital in Piccadilly was knocked down after serving for 150 years, and the site became a sunken garden.

MRI nursing was also renewed, especially by Margaret Sparshott, who in 1907 took up the post of Lady Superintendent of Nurses at the MRI. She had radical plans to improve the lot of nurses, thus encouraging more young women to enter the profession. With the backing of the Board of Governors she succeeded in raising nursing salaries, bringing them more into line with London salaries and the pay-scales recommended by the College of Nursing; she also gained a clutch of additional appointments to staff the new Oxford Road hospital. Her other major initiatives were to plan a syllabus of lectures to probationer nurses in the Infirmary, to be given by both consultants and senior nursing staff, and to encourage the

Figure 1. By the end of the nineteenth century, the Manchester Royal Infirmary was under intense critical scrutiny, in large part due to its cramped conditions and its location at the heart of a large, dirty, industrial city.

building of a residential training school for nurses in the grounds of the Infirmary. The new 'Sparshott House' opened in the late 1920s around the same time that a Nursing Sub-Committee was formed to assist communication between the increasingly organized nursing profession and the Honorary Consultants and Board of Governors.

The Infirmary's 'Central Branch' on Roby Street was built to appease opponents of the move by providing a central hospital for accident and emergency work only a hundred yards from the old Piccadilly site. The institution gradually evolved to also include serious surgical cases. Its role as a war hospital during the First World War consolidated its position as a first-class surgical centre with considerable capabilities for emergency work. In many ways, the Central Branch was a fully-fledged hospital in its own right at the heart of the City, but it was closed in 1943, during the Second World War, when there was neither sufficient building materials to protect it from potential bomb damage nor sufficient doctors to staff it simply as a casualty department. It was 'temporarily requisitioned' by the government as a hostel for industrial workers, but never opened again as a hospital – though the MRI continued to request its return until 1946 at least.

Oxford Road and its new hospitals

The MRI move had been a long battle but the Owens Trustees had more immediate success in creating or moving some of the smaller hospitals. A big house on the new site was turned into a small Cancer Hospital – a favourite project of one of the medical professors and of Mrs Christie, the wife of a key Whitworth executor. The professor of obstetrics and gynaecology agreed that the small charity which he served, the Southern Hospital on Upper Brook Street, would relocate to the College site; but its larger rival, St. Mary's, was not interested – they wanted to keep their independence and rebuild in town, on what is now Whitworth Street. However, when St. Mary's tried for a share in another big legacy, from the David Lewis Trustees, they were pushed towards a merger with the Southern and to rebuilding on the Owens site. The dispute became very public, and St. Mary's was much criticized in the press for putting its special interests before the public good. The eventual outcome was a single hospital charity, called St. Mary's, with *two* new buildings – one in town, on Whitworth Street at the junction with Oxford Street, opened in 1904 and used for obstetrics; the other on the Owens estate, near Whitworth Park, opened in 1910 for gynaecology cases and children.

When the MRI and St. Mary's relocated, they also became neighbours of the Eye Hospital which had thrived in the late 1860s, doubling its income in about 5 years. One of its surgeons, Dr Adolph Samelson, was a very effective organizer, if rather too independent for the Board of Management. The head nurse (and later Matron), Miss Margaret Somerville, seems to have worked as an oculist herself, and certainly knew how to encourage the Ladies Committee – then a key part of the fund-raising. By 1879, the doctors were pressing for more accommodation, and a few cottages were rented behind St. Johns Street. In 1883, a new site was taken on Oxford Road, just south of the college, and a hospital of 100 beds began work in 1885. It was opened by the long-time chairman, Alderman Philip Goldschmidt, then in his second term as Mayor of Manchester. The grand new building was a major expenditure, and there had been opposition to a move out of town; but Manchester Corporation had reduced the cost of the site by buying the front strip for road widening, and concerns about access of outpatients were met by retaining an eye clinic on St. John's Street in the heart of the City.

The Dental Hospital, from its beginning in 1883, was near the University, but that did not mean it was free of trouble or the need to move. No sooner had the hospital opened in Grosvenor Street than another group of dentists met in the Lord Mayor's parlour to found a second institution – which then took over the first, so the facility had two openings in one year. Notwithstanding this tumultuous beginning, links between the Hospital and the University developed well. The passing of the 1878 Dental Act had introduced a new Register for Licensed Dentists (an effort to exclude quacks from the trade), and once the Royal College of Surgeons gave the new hospital formal recognition as a teaching site in 1884, students began to seek instruction. As for patients, the hospital's governing body decided to open the Hospital's treatment rooms three evenings a week for the working poor, who would otherwise lose wages if attending in day-time. This scheme (which was never adopted in any ordinary hospital) proved a roaring success, and by 1887 the Hospital was treating more than 10,000 patients per year, the great majority during the evenings. The institution then had 11 students in attendance; lectures were held in the Owens College Medical School and practical instruction in the Hospital. After further increases in student numbers, the Hospital moved in 1892 to larger accommodation in Devonshire Street – a temporary move which soon proved inadequate. Pressure on resources was great, and through the pages of its Annual Reports the Dental Hospital Committee pleaded with the people of Manchester to help it protect the teeth of the City and its surroundings, by providing treatment, advice and future dentists.

By the Edwardian period, bad teeth were a prominent symptom of poor national health; nearly half of potential soldiers were rejected because of their bad teeth. Working with the Manchester and Salford Sanitary Association, the Dental Committee wrote tracts and gave public talks to raise awareness of the Dental Hospital, including their new facilities for making and fitting false teeth. 'The future of the nation depends largely upon the teeth of the people,' claimed a 1908 leaflet requesting new benefactors. And indeed, the fortunes of the Hospital and the status of its dentist were at last improving. Several large donations during the early 1900s secured a site, and a new Victoria Dental Hospital was constructed next to the University Museum on Oxford Road (of which the dental building is now a part). Built in 'Wrenaissance' style, and closely associated with the medical school which had recently established degrees and diplomas in dentistry, it proclaimed Manchester as a leader in dental education.

Most of the hospitals which settled on Oxford Road had land available for expansion, and the regular moves characteristic of small medical charities in mid-century became a thing of the past. It seems too, that as voluntary hospitals became larger, more technical and more bureaucratic, so the tussles between lay governors and leading doctors softened. In a sense, the relocations to Oxford Road symbolized the recognition that hospital medicine would be led, like the College, by a collection of scientific professionals – for whom lay philanthropists provided financial, political and managerial support, rather than detailed direction.

The Great War and after

Edwardian Manchester was known as the chief centre of the global textile industry. It was also a major national centre for engineering and chemicals, for municipal schemes such as the Ship Canal, for music, and for its new University, which ranked with London and Cambridge for physical sciences. The medical school and associated hospitals boasted some of the best clinicians in the country; they rivaled the finest London schools – for in London, the many teaching hospitals competed with each other and were only loosely related to London University.

By the start of the Great War, central government had become closely associated with medicine, not only through the sanitary effort and the concern with infant mortality c.1900, but through the sustained attention to childbirth, child welfare and worker's health. Tuberculosis services featured in the National Insurance Act of 1911, under which workers and their employers contributed to compulsory health insurance under state supervision. Workers could sign up with a general practitioner and be treated 'free'; but this scheme did not cover their dependants, or any hospital treatment except for tuberculosis. Hospitals continued to rely on subscriptions, and in industrial towns the organized contributions from the working classes became increasingly important.

The waging of war transformed the country for five years. In Manchester, as in other large cities, many colleges, mansions, sanatoria and asylums were taken-over for wounded soldiers sent home on trains from France. Special hospitals were created for the treatment of shell-shock, soldier's heart, and injuries of bones and nerves, and the army's emphasis on restoring function helped establish new medical and surgical specialists such as orthopaedics. Grangethorpe, a mansion near Platt Fields was used for nerve injuries and gave valuable experience to John Stopford and Harry Platt, two recent Manchester graduates who were to emerge as key figures in Manchester medicine – Stopford as Professor of Anatomy, Dean of Medicine, and then Vice-Chancellor of the University; Platt as the national leader in orthopaedics. Their friend Geoffrey Jefferson became equally renowned in neurosurgery.

Hospitals for women and for children were less directly affected, except where they received government money to set up Special Clinics for venereal diseases, then threatening the strength of the army. St. Mary's was also offered private money for a Birth Control clinic, probably by Humphrey Roe (brother of aircraft manufacturer A. V. Roe), then married to Marie Stopes – University palaeo-botanist turned reformer of sexual life. St. Mary's refused; it was not sympathetic to feminist ideals. A Babies' Hospital, later the Duchess of York Hospital in Burnage, was founded in 1914 in a house in Chorlton. It was run by a few women doctors and other feminists, devoted to infant welfare and frustrated by the exclusion of women doctors from resident posts at the Infirmary and St. Mary's. And as we noted earlier, it was also during the war that Booth Hall was assigned as a children's hospital when the three Poor Law unions were merged.

When the war ended in 1918, the cotton trade experienced a boom, but its 'bust' in 1920 proved the beginning of a long and terminal decline. During the war, textile manufacture had rapidly increased in India, Japan and the USA. Lancashire could not compete; the mill towns became economically 'depressed,' though Manchester itself was somewhat buffered by its chemical, engineering, finance, education and service trades. For Lancashire, the era of big local charity from textiles and engineering was ending. The major donation to Manchester hospitals in the 1920s and 1930s came from a new trade – from Sir Samuel Turner, the Rochdale businessman and head of Turner and Newall asbestos manufacturers, who paid for a new dental hospital.

In the two decades after the Great War, hospital medicine was dominated by the development of medical specialisms and extensions of government support. The hospitals under the Poor Law were upgraded to include more acute work and even some private patients. Booth Hall focused on the diseases commonest among the children of the poor, such as bronchitis and tuberculosis, whooping cough and measles, scabies and ringworm. A new 'open air' block was opened in 1927: the large verandahs and windows exposed the children to the sun, or at least to 'fresh' air. Such architecture was common in the sanatoria then being developed by local authorities across the country, and in the open-air schools for children with weak constitutions.

The early twentieth century concern with infants was extended to maternity care, promoted especially by women's groups who wanted more hospital confinements, both for mothers with difficult pregnancies and for those whose home conditions were poor. In many of the industrial towns, municipal maternity homes were established for such mothers, often in the former homes of departed textile magnates. In Manchester, where the maternity services at St. Mary's were grossly overcrowded, some extra beds were provided nearby in Victoria Park in a mansion taken-over as a convalescent home for mothers after birth. But such was the pressure on St. Mary's that some mothers who had booked-in there were sent to Crumpsall hospital. In the mid-thirties, one such mother was moved from St. Mary's immediately after an emergency delivery, and then died at Crumpsall. The consequent public scandal forced better co-ordination between hospitals. By then St. Mary's was planning a big new maternity hospital, to be built in Rusholme behind their Gynaecology branch, just south of the Infirmary.

By then too, Crumpsall was a municipal hospital, as were Withington and Booth Hall. The Poor Law had been ended by an Act of 1929 and the local workhouse hospitals transferred in 1931 to the Public Health Committee of Manchester City, where they came under the authority of the Medical Officer of Health (MOH). The MOH was already responsible for clinics, sanatoria and the Monsall Hospital for infectious diseases, developed from the 1870s as a branch of the Infirmary but later transferred to the city. The MOH and the City Council were keen to develop specialist services in its hospitals, and to collaborate with the doctors who led the teaching hospitals. Manchester became nationally known in the later thirties for effective co-ordination between the voluntary and statutory sectors, and this was to provide a basis for later co-ordination under the NHS.

The Infirmary and St. Mary's rationalized their co-habitation in 1935; the Infirmary gave up its gynaecology wards, and St. Mary's agreed to use the Infirmary's laboratory. The anatomist John Stopford was now the head of the University – a powerful politician, keen to promote sciences and the new clinical specialisms. His student contemporaries Harry Platt and Geoffrey Jefferson had established their international reputations in orthopaedics and neurosurgery, at Salford Royal and Ancoats respectively. Stopford brought them into the Infirmary to set up special departments, aided by the hospital co-ordination schemes. In obstetrics too, Manchester was a leader of specialization: Walter Fletcher Shaw at St. Mary's was one of the founders of the Royal College of Obstetrics and Gynaecology. In the treatment of cancer, Manchester became internationally renowned for radium treatment. The small cancer hospital set up in early 1890s on the Owens estate, and later named for Mrs Christie, had been merged with the Holt Radium Institute, which had originated in 1914 as a campaign to buy radium for use in the hospitals of Manchester. The combined institution built a neo-classical hospital in a southern suburb, Withington. Its new director, Ralston Paterson, a Scot who had trained at the Mayo clinic in the USA, arranged radiotherapy services for most of the municipalities of the region, so prefiguring the regionalism of the NHS.

The Christie Hospital and Holt Radium Institute moved away from the teaching hospitals, politically as well as physically, but the rest of the hospitals were increasingly connected to the University and its medical school. Nowhere was this clearer than for the dental hospital, where student numbers had increased rapidly after the Great War, from about 50 in total to about 160, and they continued to climb. The 'new' Victoria Dental Hospital of 1908 was over-run, and its museum of dental anatomy was scrapped to make room for an X-ray suite donated by Miss Hyde in 1920. Negotiations for a University take-over began in 1930, and in 1933 the University took responsibility for the management of both Dental School and Hospital. Under the new arrangements the Hospital gained a whole-time professorship in Dental Surgery, who was also the Director of the Dental Hospital, and the first of a clutch of whole-time research and teaching appointments. Specialists in relatively new fields such as plastic surgery and speech therapy were appointed to the hospital, and ancillary departments and clinics, such as oral pathology and paediatric dentistry, were squeezed-in alongside the more established dental work.

Although the University had agreed that the Dental Hospital needed to be extended, it baulked at the Charity Committee's insistence that the only remedy was once again to build anew. Only after the large private donation by Samuel Turner was a new building provided, on Bridge Street, behind the main University buildings. It was to have been officially opened in June 1940, but

Figure 2. The Private Patients Home was opened in the Infirmary grounds in 1937 to provide separate areas for those able to pay the costs of their care. The end balconies gave a certain architectural flair to the building, and served as sundecks for patients.

MANCHESTER ROYAL INFIRMARY

1 DOCTOR · 1752 · 300 NURSES · 355,996 PATIENTS ATTENDANCES · 280 DOMESTICS · 1850 · 19 DOCTORS

45 VISITING SPECIALISTS · 36 RESIDENT DOCTORS

22 LABORATORY, CLINICAL & RESEARCH STAFF · 1938 · 16 MASSAGE STAFF

Figure 3. Staff of the MRI in the late 1930s dressed-up to celebrate the long history of the Infirmary, reflecting on the growth of medical specialization, research, and nursing care

the Second World War intervened: the opening ceremony was cancelled but the hospital was at work from May. Seven months later it was bombed during an air-raid, and passed much of the rest of the war without windows; but it took on numerous war duties allocated by the Ministry of Health, including routine dentistry for all service personnel, evacuees, refugees, and war-related factory workers. The Ministry also set up a Jaw and Plastic Unit at the new institution, and much work on facial disfigurement was undertaken in conjunction with the prosthetics department. The Dental Hospital also co-operated with the Infirmary for some surgical cases, and so did the Manchester Foot Hospital, on Anson Street (near Victoria Park), which had been founded in 1920 to train chiropodists and give free treatment to the needy. Like the dental hospital it did not have beds, but ran daytime and evening outpatient clinics. Foot problems, though important to many, were even less glamorous than those of teeth, and this hospital also struggled to attract donors.

A final hospital facility was added to the Oxford Road site just before the outbreak of the Second World War. In 1932 the Board of Management of the Infirmary had announced their plans for a Private Patients' Home (PPH) to be built on the eastern boundary of their site. It was: 'urgently required to meet an insistent demand' for pay-beds. To the Chairman of the Infirmary Board, Walter Cobbett, it seemed: 'almost a ridiculous anomaly that a panel patient should obtain as a matter of course and at a nominal or no cost a complete

18   COMMUNITY, PROFESSIONS AND BUSINESS

investigation involving the services of an eminent specialist, X-ray examination, blood tests, electrical tests, etc., whilst no such combined services can be obtained in a Private Hospital or Ward by a patient willing to pay for them.' When the PPH opened in 1937, a sliding pay scale meant that the beds were accessible to the lower middle classes as well as richer groups. The PPH was testimony to the success of the 'modern' hospital – well-to-do patients now chose the technologies and medical care offered by the hospital, over the comforts of care in their own homes. The MRI now covered all classes – more or less – and specialists could expect to earn some private income 'on site'.

The Second World War and the planning of the NHS

During the First World War, medical organization was improvised; for the Second it was planned, and the planning soon included future, peace-time needs. Practically all the country's hospitals were brought under the Emergency Hospital Service, which paid for the doctors and emptied many of the beds to await military and civilian casualties. By 1940, doctors and others were already planning for a post-war world, and many who had experienced the crushing of public hopes and governmental ambitions in the recession after the Great War were determined that, this time, the plans would work. Everyone concentrated on hospitals rather than general practice and public health, though it was commonly assumed that the national insurance provision for general practice would be extended to wives and children, thus covering most of the population. Hospitals were the most exciting and progressive area of medicine, but also the most expensive and immediately problematic. Many charity hospitals had struggled financially during the 1920s and 1930s; only those with strong Workers' Contribution Schemes were at all secure, and they were not the prestige institutions.

To those who loved the municipal services, which had rapidly developed in the former workhouse hospitals in the late 30s, it seemed clear that the town councils should gradually take-over the funding and direction of the voluntary hospitals. However, the advocates of voluntary hospital independence, fearing that charity finances could not be restored after the wartime state support, argued for government funding, like that for Universities or the BBC, which would preserve substantial professional autonomy. The wartime coalition government favoured the former course. After the 1942 report on social security by William Beveridge, they agreed that hospital services, like GP services, would be free at the point of use. That much was generally popular, but the supporters of voluntary hospitals, and especially the elite doctors, were vehemently opposed to municipal control. Churchill's conservative cabinet which took over at the end of the war, steered towards the second alternative, although they feared being seen as reneging on wartime promises. But Churchill lost the general election in 1945, and Aneurin Bevan became Minister of Health in Atlee's Labour government.

Bevan was a radical, but unlike many Labour ministers, he was not attached to the municipal tradition that had been central to state funding in the first half of the century. He threw out the results of the complex wartime negotiations, and instead planned to *nationalize* all the hospitals. The voluntary hospitals would come under national control exercised though regional and local boards on which doctors, philanthropists, and councillors would all be represented. The teaching hospitals would report directly to the Ministry of Health, and elite doctors would get special financial awards to make sure they stayed in the system, at least for part of their working weeks. Many leading consultants recognized a 'good deal', and medical university teachers welcomed a salaried system that would ensure substantial professional input into decisions about staffing and funding. Municipalities resented the loss of 'their' hospitals, and the separation of these hospitals from other health services; but most of the large municipalities were Labour controlled and agreed to the nationalization. The public was enthusiastic.

Around Manchester, the NHS arrangements built on the interwar developments. Stopford, still head of the University, became chair of the Manchester Regional Hospital Board, where Harry Platt was also influential. The Regional Board then grouped the hospitals into districts, each under a Hospital Management Committee (HMC) The Christie, after losing a battle to have its own HMC, was grouped with Withington and Baguley Sanatorium in South Manchester HMC. Ancoats and Crumpsall came under the HMC for North Manchester. The children's hospitals were all assigned to a single special HMC which covered the Royal Manchester Children's Hospital, the Duchess of York Hospital for Babies, Booth Hall, and Monsall (though Monsall, the isolation hospital for infectious diseases, contained as many adults as children).

The medical advisors to the Regional Board were mostly consultants at the teaching hospitals, and the regional medical administrator, Dr F.N. Marshall, was a Stopford protégé. Thus the university medical elite had a double advantage – they helped run the hospitals for the rest of the region, while their own hospitals preserved a special autonomy. The central teaching hospitals became the United Manchester Hospitals and reported directly to the Ministry. Now, as never before in peace time, the teaching hospitals would be supported by taxation – for the good of all, both rich and poor.

CHAPTER TWO

The NHS and the Teaching Hospitals, 1945–1960

THE IMMEDIATE post–Second World War years were tough for the MRI, as they were for most of the nation's hospitals. Money, labour and building materials were in short supply, and making good the losses of the war was a slow and difficult process. That large numbers of returning servicemen sought to resume or begin their medical studies, put considerable additional strain on cramped accommodation and the bomb-damaged hospital. But hopes were high and plans were ambitious. The new National Health Service was put into operation on 5 July 1948. Overnight the nation's hospitals, both municipal and charity-funded, became part of a nationalized service, the main branch of the tri-partite NHS – hospital medicine alongside public health and general practice.

On this 'Appointed Day', the MRI ended almost 200 years as a voluntary hospital; all the Infirmary's property and equipment became the property of the state. Aneurin Bevan came to Manchester to mark the occasion but did not visit the MRI. He went to Park Hospital, Davyhulme — which had been opened under the Poor Law in 1928, transferred to Lancashire County Council and used by the American services during the recent war.

Like other major teaching hospitals, the MRI was now to be controlled by a management committee directly answerable to the Minister of Health. This was one of the several 'perks' that teaching hospitals had gained in negotiations over the NHS. They also retained control of their own endowment funds and could use them for services or research. A limited number of pay beds were retained within the nationalized service, mostly in the teaching hospitals. The Infirmary continued to operate the Private Patients' Home, established in the grounds of the hospital in the 1930s. The PPH flourished during the 1950s (even seeing a significant rise in waiting times), showing that not everyone was ready or willing to enrol in state medicine.

Following the Appointed Day, the MRI became part of a 'hospital-group' – the United Manchester Hospitals or UMH. This comprised the Manchester Royal Infirmary, the Private Patients' Home, and Barnes Convalescent Hospital in Cheadle; St. Mary's Hospitals at Whitworth Street and Whitworth Park; the Manchester Royal Eye Hospital; the Dental Hospital of Manchester; and the Manchester Foot Hospital. The new UMH had its own Board of Governors, headed by Mr Colin Skinner, who had been Treasurer to the MRI since 1929. This Board reported to the Ministry and was meant to oversee the administrations of the individual hospitals, ensuring comprehensive and standardized provision of teaching and services. But it would be several years before the hospitals of the UMH amalgamated in a meaningful sense.

The Oxford Road site after the Second World War

The Oxford Road hospital site had taken a battering during the war. Most strikingly, part of the Infirmary's magnificent frontage had been destroyed by bombing, as had the teaching block and

Figure 4. Preparing for war.

Figure 5. Like many industrial cities in Britain, Manchester suffered from numerous bombing raids in the Second World War. The Infirmary did not escape, as can be seen in the extensive damage to the Nurses' New Home.

part of the X-ray Department. There was also substantial damage to the neighbouring Manchester Royal Eye Hospital, where a bomb had killed two members of staff and seriously damaged the front of the hospital. The Infirmary's New Home for nurses had suffered extensive bomb-damage to its recently completed Great Hall. Within the constraints imposed by national shortages of building material, the Nurses' New Home and part of the damaged X-Ray Department were quickly patched up.

During the war, St. Mary's Whitworth *Park* branch, located beside the Manchester Royal Infirmary, at the south end of the Oxford Road site, had not been considered as immediately at risk. But the main maternity hospital stood in Whitworth *Street*, near Oxford Road railway station and not far from the Town Hall. It seemed very vulnerable and was closed for most of the war. In its place, large country mansions were taken over for expectant mothers: one in Prestbury for women from city centre 'danger areas', and one in Adlington for wives of men serving in the forces; another fifty beds for emergency and morbid pregnancies were established at the Whitworth Park branch for women unable to travel out to Cheshire. But in fact, both the St. Mary's hospitals escaped enemy bombardment.

The Medical Board had planned to build a new, combined St. Mary's hospital on the Oxford Road site but money was scarce after the war, and in the meantime the Whitworth Street hospital was remodelled to update its sanitation system, staff amenities, antenatal ward and sterilization facilities. In 1947 a new 'premature baby station' was opened to provide a therapeutic environment of purified, humidified air at a constant temperature. In keeping with the contemporary investment in technology, an X-ray department was also built during this refit. When Whitworth Park followed its sister institution and gained its own radiologist in 1952, the St. Mary's hospitals became independent of the MRI for radiological services.

Plans to build a Neurological Institute at the MRI had been much discussed in the early 1930s. Manchester's eminent neurological surgeon, Sir Geoffrey Jefferson, had argued that a concentration of regional services at the MRI – a hospital long famous for treating 'nerves' – would ensure excellence in both treatment and research. In 1950 the Neurological Block was opened, with a state of the art Neurosurgical Theatre and its own Neuroradiological Department. But, aside from the addition of a new floor to the Pathology Department for use by Clinical Pathology in 1958, there was little other building in the MRI during the 1940s and 1950s. Though a post-war survey had recommended several Infirmary buildings for partial or total demolition, some of them, including the bomb-damaged Teaching Block, had in the meantime to be made useful.

In July 1950 the Board of Governors of the UMH resolved to convert the Gaskell Nursing Home into a psychiatric facility, providing in-patient beds and outpatient clinics as part of a new Psychiatry Department. Previously, mental patients had mostly been confined in Asylums outside the towns, or in special workhouses wards, but mental health services had been brought under the new NHS, and in the Manchester region especially, facilities were being developed in general hospitals to reduce the 'distance' between psychiatry and the rest of medicine. The MRI also built five huts between the medical and surgical corridors to house facilities for other new University departments, involving some notable clinicians and trainees.

The UMH Board of Governors lacked the financial means to make more general alterations to the MRI building, which, though more recent than most in the region, seemed increasingly archaic. One Manchester physician remembered his impressions of the Infirmary upon his arrival as a student in the mid 1940s: 'the first thing was the structure of the place which was so very odd. It was built when people believed you should allow cold air to blow through it, which either destroyed or distributed the germs and diluted them so much

Figure 6. *oppostie* The new Infirmary was constructed according to the 'pavilion' design, with long wards fanning out from central corridors. Designs like this were common in British hospitals built before the Second World War; they originated in the mid nineteenth century and were promoted by Florence Nightingale in the belief that fresh air would prevent the spread of disease.

that they didn't do anybody any damage! So all the corridors were open from the waist up [to the roof] …in between wards and along the main junctional corridors along the length of the building. It was not the sort of place where you hung about in the middle of the night!'

It wasn't just the original buildings and bomb-damage that were causing problems however; 'Platt's Plaster Palace', the Orthopaedics Block opened in 1938 for the famous Manchester surgeon Harry Platt, was crumbling within ten years. In contrast to the world-famous facility it housed, the modernist Block was a testament to poor workmanship and design. The substandard accommodation across the Infirmary undoubtedly affected the morale of staff and patients, and concerns over safety and security were common on the open site; but the reputation of the Infirmary held firm. As one nurse who trained at the MRI in this period remarked: 'it's not as

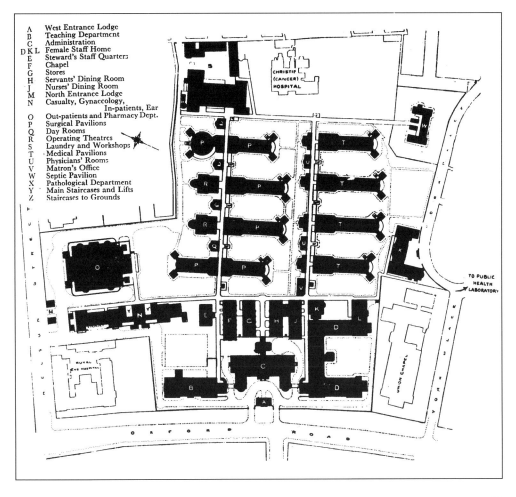

A   West Entrance Lodge
B   Teaching Department
C   Administration
D K L Female Staff Home
E   Steward's Staff Quarters
F   Chapel
G   Stores
H   Servants' Dining Room
J   Nurses' Dining Room
M   North Entrance Lodge
N   Casualty, Gynaecology,
            In-patients, Ear
O   Out-patients and Pharmacy Dept.
P   Surgical Pavilions
Q   Day Rooms
R   Operating Theatres
S   Laundry and Workshops
T   Medical Pavilions
U   Physicians' Rooms
V   Matron's Office
W   Septic Pavilion
X   Pathological Department
Y   Main Staircases and Lifts
Z   Staircases to Grounds

if the hospitals looked different elsewhere!' Indeed, most of Britain's national health estate was badly in need of renovation.

Supernumeraries, specialist posts and the Spens Report

The NHS proved beneficial for doctors, especially hospital consultants who were now paid for their hospital work. All medical staff had to be reviewed to determine their grades. In smaller hospitals many doctors were classed as 'Senior Hospital Medical Officers', rather than Consultants, while others left hospital practice to become full-time NHS general practitioners. In the MRI, as in other prominent teaching hospitals, almost all the main clinicians were recognised and paid as Consultants. They were free to do some private practice, and many worked 8 or 9 half-days a week for the NHS, keeping 2 or 3 sessions for private work. A few top consultants also gained 'merit awards' – by a secretly determined system of pay designed to compensate senior clinicians for any substantial losses of income from private practice. These included the clinical Professors, who were now more able to devote most of their time to their hospital practice, research and teaching.

To accommodate young doctors who had returned from the services, while simultaneously anticipating the likely demands of the NHS, the teaching hospitals were required to provide 'supernu-merary' posts for trainee consultants – but opinions differed as to their utility. Manchester University's Vice-Chancellor John Stopford, after observing the operation of the scheme for few months, rather irritably asked his colleagues on the Board of the UMH to explain what and how supernumeraries contributed, either to patient care or to the education of students. His surgeon colleague, Harry Platt, claimed that supernumeraries were little more than 'glorified spectators', who took up space in already cramped working conditions. For others however, the post-war influx of demobilized medical officers and the new legislation for the NHS, had provided a welcome increase in middle and senior level staff. The new, salaried, Professor of Medicine, Robert Platt, argued strongly that an aggregation of supernumeraries, Senior House Officers and additional Consultants would increase the amount of high quality research at the Infirmary. He believed that a previous lack of higher-grade medical personnel had contributed to a 'neglect' of clinical research, and thought that a hospital such as the MRI, with its numerous special departments, could easily absorb the expanding specialist grades.

At the Dental School, there were few if any supernumeraries. The armed services were very slow to demobilize dental officers, and a lack of personnel at the Dental School in the immediate post-war years threatened both the preparations for the NHS and a number of nascent projects, including the Children's Clinic established to provide dental care for some 1,200 schoolchildren in the region, and the Nuffield Foundation-sponsored Department of Preventative Dentistry and Research which was to be affiliated with the new University Department of Child Health.

Most returning doctors were absorbed into Second Chief or Clinical Assistant positions in the expanding special and outpatient departments. Other demobilized officers went, as Robert Platt had hoped, into the new academic specialty units of the MRI. This emphasis upon research by the supernumeraries was in keeping not only with Platt's views but also with government thinking on hospital training posts.

The 1948 Report of the Interdepartmental Committee on the Remuneration of Consultants and Specialists (Spens Committee) had made recommendations to counter the highly uneven geographic and disciplinary spread of specialists. One of the key concerns was consultant equity – to ensure comparable grades and comparable pay between different branches of specialty practice, and between different hospitals, despite differences in pre-NHS prestige. And indeed, the new NHS was generally successful in developing specialist services, not least in connection with medical schools. But specialist supply was not easy to plan, in part because the need for trainees on the wards did not necessarily fit the future needs for qualified staff. The higher availability of merit awards in some disciplines over others, and the problems posed by an overstuffed senior registrar tier, were two of the many difficulties in the implementation of Spens. Across the country, its infrastructure for specialist planning and assessment was later radically altered or abandoned.

In nursing too, the post-war years saw many new developments, but the NHS soon ran up against a serious shortage of qualified nurses, prompting hospitals across the UMH group to make frequent appeals for new recruits. In St. Mary's the problem was furthermore exacerbated by a chronic shortage of trained midwives.

The United Manchester Hospitals School of Nursing

In 1938 the Infirmary and St. Mary's had set up a Joint Committee to discuss a co-ordinated training scheme for their nurses. The plan was on hold throughout the war, but in 1950, at the ceremony marking the restoration of the Nurses' Great Hall, the Infirmary chairman, Sir Walter Cobbett, handed out the last of the badges and prizes to bear the name and symbols of the Manchester Royal Infirmary School of Nursing. In January 1950 the scheme for a Joint Nurse

Training School for the United Manchester Hospitals was finally put into operation after the Board gained the approval of the national General Nurses Council. The new School also included training at the Barnes Hospital and the Royal Eye Hospital (where students could also gain an Ophthalmic Certificate during the fourth year of their training). The MRI's long-serving Matron, Miss Duff Grant, was chosen as the first Principal. Henceforth, all nurses training at the School did so under the aegis of the UMH, as their newly designed badges showed.

Though training was rationalized across the teaching hospitals, nurses still learned on the wards. The new NHS had considered a more radical departure – that nurses, like intending doctors, should be students for much of their training. In national and regional negotiations, however, the 'nursing interest' was usually represented by senior matrons apprehensive about the potential loss of labour-force on the wards. Decades would pass before any such plans were realized for nurses in general; but as we shall see, during the 1950s and 1960s Manchester University pioneered diploma and degree courses intended to produce leaders and teachers for the profession.

The matrons' worries were all the more understandable given the shortage of nurses, albeit somewhat offset by immigration from Eastern Europe, and then from the Commonwealth. In the early 1950s, the UMH School of Nurses was required to increase its intake, even though the accommodation was cramped and shabby. Work on the new Nursing School, built next to the Nurses' New Home, did not begin until 1959. While the theoretical part of the curriculum remained for the most part unchanged during these early years of the School, the practical side was diversified. From 1952, student nurses could take a secondment to the Baguley Chest Hospital (an ex-municipal sanatorium). In 1954 a similar arrangement was made with the Royal Manchester Children's Hospital (Pendlebury) for experience in paediatric nursing, and a year later, a scheme with the Booth Hall Hospital for Sick Children meant that after a period of four years training a student could gain a dual qualification as a State Registered Nurse and as a Registered Sick Children's Nurse. Additional links made later with other local hospitals (for example, with Cheadle Royal for experience in nursing the mentally ill), reflected national trends in co-operative nurse training.

The Board of Governors of the UMH were also committed to nursing research within the new School, and grants were given to Sister Tutors for travel to Europe and the United States to report on innovations in nursing education. In 1958 the Royal College of Nursing in Edinburgh held the nation's first course for Clinical Tutors, and the UMH sent one of their nurses, Miss J. W. Charleston. Upon her return to Manchester, Miss Charleston shared her instruction with the ward sisters, to implement new methods for teaching student nurses.

The University and the transformation of academic medicine

Before the war, all sixteen British universities had governed their own affairs and the only government interest was to grant charters and to distribute a limited amount of cash via the University Grants Committee (UGC). But heavy government investment in research and development during the Second World War focused national attention on the universities, as did their role in the operation of the Emergency Medical Service (accompanying the Emergency Hospitals Service). Whereas before the war, the UGC had given an annual block grant to each university to spend as it wished, from the mid 1940s large additional grants became available for specific purposes – but subject to the approval of special UGC specialist sub-committees. Thus for the first time, government took a major role in the planning and control of British universities; and other organizations also worked to strengthen this bond.

For instance, in 1939 the banker William Goodenough and his friend Lord Nuffield (William Morris), the car-maker and philanthropist, had founded a new trust to help co-ordinate hospital services throughout the provinces. Funded by shares in Nuffield's Morris Motors Company, and with the blessing of the Ministry of Health, the 'Nuffield Trust' encouraged hospital rationalization, and became a major source of grants and donations to individual institutions, including the MRI and UMH.

During the war, when many aspects of post-war life were being debated and planned, several of the doctors, academics and philanthropists who were active in the Nuffield Trust were asked to form a new Governmental Committee to consider post-war reconstruction of the medical schools. Chaired by Goodenough, with Manchester's John Stopford as Vice-Chair, the Committee was dominated by research-clinicians interested in the further expansion of British academic medicine. This was their great chance to introduce whole-time clinical professorships devoted to teaching and research, a goal of many reformers since the Edwardian period, and one unsuccessfully attempted in Manchester after the First World War. The NHS funding of salaries and merit awards for hospital consultants would finally make this possible, and within eight years of the publication of Goodenough's findings, all but one of Britain's teaching hospitals possessed academic units in the three major branches. Fifty-five new whole-time chairs in clinical subjects were created in Britain between 1947 and 1952, allowing the development of laboratories and other facilities for clinical research.

Progress was much more limited, however, in the Goodenough Committee's second set of concerns: the promotion of 'social medicine' by the reform of the clinical curriculum, increased support of public health, and the founding of 'health centres' for general practitioners. In the late 1940s, several such schemes were afoot, but nearly all were to flounder in the 1950s. Manchester University tried to start a department of general practice capable of research and systematic teaching, but they relied on the GPs already practising in the area of the new facility – who proved not to be research-minded.

For hospital medicine, if not for general practice, the early NHS was built around regional centres of excellence, generally the teaching hospitals. The final Goodenough Report stated that: 'The spirit of education must permeate the *whole* of the health service, and that service must be so designed and conducted that, among other things, it secures for medical education the necessary staff, accommodation, equipment and facilities. Medical education cannot be regarded as merely incidental to the hospital service.' The reformers aimed to encourage life-long learning in British medicine, and the ongoing training of qualified doctors was to be encouraged through compulsory pre-registration appointments, and a significant expansion of postgraduate and 'refresher'-type courses. In the first NHS Bill, these educational and research issues had been rather overlooked by the civil servants, but the reformers had good political connections and rapidly secured revisions, especially for the teaching hospitals. Provision was further extended through the Medical Act of 1950, and all types of hospitals were to be brought into the effort.

Many medical schools, including Manchester, then appointed postgraduate Deans to set up local courses and links with regional hospitals. This linking of central and peripheral hospitals offered a solution to a number of problems – from encouraging money to flow into the still relatively impoverished former municipal sector, to ensuring the adequate provision of teaching material for clinical students, and training opportunities for their graduate and practitioner seniors. If, as the Goodenough Report argued, future progress in medicine depended on the integration of basic sciences with *all* clinical teaching, then closer bonding between universities and teaching hospitals was also imperative.

In Manchester, such efforts were guided by Stopford and his supporters. Their vision was also evident in the redevelopment plans

Figure 7. John Sebastian Bach Stopford (Baron Stopford of Fallowfield) was a professor of anatomy, head of the Manchester Medical School, and then head of the University. During the interwar and post-Second World War years, he championed reform of medical education and research, and became Vice-Chair of the Goodenough Committee, which advised the government on the postwar reconstruction of British medical schools. Under the NHS, he was the first chairman of the Manchester Regional Hospital Board.

for the city of Manchester, which had been published in 1945. This was hardly surprising, for the Chairman of the University Council, the industrialist Ernest Darwin Simon, was a key member of the City Council and the major local advocate of town planning. In retrospect, the Manchester Plan is both shocking and impressive: the Gothic town hall, now so prized, might have been replaced by a 'machine for governance', along with most of the Victorian town centre. But the plan also embodied the integration of the University and teaching hospitals into the central fabric of the city – an aspiration which we strive to realize, sixty years on.

The plan, published before the NHS was finalized, envisaged a 'Hospital City' on the Oxford Road site: 'The Manchester Royal Infirmary, St. Mary's Hospital, the Tuberculosis Clinic and the Royal Eye Hospital [would] form an established nucleus for a comprehensive medical and surgical centre … a major centre for teaching and research … [combining] the character of a regional consultative centre and professional headquarters. It would include those specialized facilities which cannot economically be duplicated in nearby boroughs and urban districts.' A 'Manchester Federation of Hospitals' was to embrace the regional headquarters of every branch of medicine and surgery, to which the various general hospitals of the city and region could look for help, and to which any cases requiring special facilities could be transferred. The Oxford Road Hospital City would thus contain: 'a general teaching hospital with medical and surgical units and departments, a maternity and women's hospital, eye and skin hospital, ear, nose and throat hospitals, institutes of child health and neurology, and departments of cardiology, metabolic medicine, chest surgery, haematology, urology, gastroenterology, rheumatic diseases, plastic surgery and industrial and social medicine, as well as such technical services as clinical pathology and bacteriology, diagnostic radiology and radiotherapy.' It seems likely that Harry Platt had a hand in these plans, and that he drew on his experience of major American hospitals.

In terms of teaching and research, the MRI remained the most prominent of Manchester's hospitals, but St. Mary's hospital developed rapidly as an academic centre, helped by its new Professorial Unit and its University Department for Paediatrics. Other hospitals in the region were traditionally used for undergraduate teaching in certain special subjects – for instance, the Royal Manchester Children's Hospital, the Manchester and Salford Hospital for Skin Diseases and St. Luke's Clinic for venereal diseases, Booth Hall Hospital for Sick Children and the Monsall fever hospital – but the Infirmary continued to be the great selling point for Manchester medicine. Through the pages of the University prospectus, would-be medical students were wooed with promises of unusually close contact with a large and varied patient intake. Would-be researchers were increasingly attracted by the many new academic units springing up around the site.

Clinical research and the Infirmary's new university departments

Pre-war plans for a closer union between the University and the UMH took a significant step forward with the appointment of four whole-time clinical professors with very limited private practice – in Medicine (1946, Robert Platt); Surgery (1947, Alan Boyd); Child Health (1947, Wilfred Gaisford); and Psychiatry (1949, E. W. Anderson). They were provided with special resources ranging from laboratories, to experimental animal facilities, to whole-time clinical research assistants. In keeping with the pattern of specialization across the hospital, the wards of the professorial units tended to take patients suffering from conditions consonant with the research interests of the staff. So for example, the Medical Professorial Unit, although a general medical ward, became in effect the MRI's 'renal ward', because this was the specialist interest of its head, Robert Platt and of his assistant (and Platt's successor as Professor of Medicine) Douglas Black. Similarly, Boyd's general surgical unit focused on the experimental surgery and pathology of the peripheral vascular system.

The University also set up five other specialist departments around this period – run by 'part-time' professors or directors already on the staff, aided by whole-time, research-oriented assistants. In this way the University helped the MRI upgrade and expand its facilities in Neurology (Professor from 1939, Geoffrey Jefferson), Orthopaedic Surgery (1939, Harry Platt), Cardiology (1946, John Bramwell), Clinical Haematology (1946, John Wilkinson), and Oto-Laryngology (1947, Victor Lambert). That Stopford had been Professor of Anatomy, Dean of Medicine, and was now Vice Chancellor of the University and chair of the Regional Hospital Board, and that Harry Platt and Jefferson were his friends from student days helped with the academic–clinical–governmental articulations that were so crucial in the years around the Second World War. All three were international figures, serving on many national committees. Jefferson, for example, chaired the clinical research committee of the MRC, and Platt became President of the Royal College of Surgeons. But all three remained devoted to Manchester medicine.

Another major post-war venture was the University Research Centre for the Study of Chronic Rheumatism, founded in 1948 with a generous donation from the Nuffield Trust. The Centre was directed on the pathology side by Stephen Baker (the University's Professor of Pathology and Pathological Anatomy who was given a special Chair in Osteopathology), and on the clinical side by Dr J.H. Kellgren. It was with Baker that a young orthopaedic surgeon, John Charnley, undertook extensive research on the fixation of joints – before he moved to the former tuberculosis hospital at Wrightington to develop his (world-famous) artificial hip. Upon Baker's retirement in 1954, Kellgren took overall control of the Centre and became Professor of Rheumatology, the first in Britain. As we will discuss in the next section, the Research Centre was an important achievement for Manchester and a symbol of the MRI's involvement in national plans for the growth of academic medicine.

It should not be forgotten however, that much new clinical research was accomplished outside the professorial units and special centres. So for instance, research on diseases of the colon, special investigations in urology, and studies of gastric function were ongoing in the 'general' surgical wards, whilst on the medical side, endocrinology and diabetes studies were prominent. Ancillary departments also emerged to 'service' the new specialties; even the seemingly mundane Department of Catering developed a Dietetic strand which became important to the researchers of the hospital, not least to the renal and hypertension workers. Similarly, the Department of Speech Therapy was established specifically to service the patients in the increasingly sophisticated departments of Oto-Larygology and Neurology who required ever more elaborate follow-up care. Another new department – Medical Illustration – reflected the enormous expansion in demand for photographs, slides and transparencies for teaching, clinical recording and research. Formerly all illustrations had been provided by the University, while photography was done part-time by an X-ray technician. The hospital had been fortunate to employ Dorothy Davison, the doyenne of medical artists, who had come to the attention of the University when sketching in the Manchester Museum. She was devoted to Geoffrey Jefferson, for whom she did hundreds of drawings of neurosurgery – many of which survive in the University medical archive.

Clinical research was not just concerned with clinical trials, laboratories and animal research, it also involved detailed follow-up care and combined, integrated therapeutic approaches which could be nurtured under the NHS in spite of strained resources and cramped accommodation. A centralized system of record keeping developed through a new office opened in the Main Out-Patient Department in 1955. This innovation also made hospital attendance more pleasant for patients, as did the introduction of evening visiting on the wards (two visitors allowed per patient, 7.00pm to 7.30 pm!), and the introduction of a WVS shop trolley service and a library service.

By the end of the 1950s the UMH group hospitals were well established as regional centres, commanding tertiary referrals from other consultant physicians and surgeons throughout the North West, along the lines outlined in the 1945 *Manchester Plan* for the development of the City.

The Manchester Centre for Rheumatism Research

By the time of the Second World War, rheumatism had achieved great political significance in Britain. In 1939, for instance, one third of all National Health Insurance payments were for chronic rheumatism, and the disease was perceived as a serious and growing threat to the industrial health of the country. The post-war Labour government sought allies to tackle this national problem. A Ministry of Health Sub-Committee on Chronic Rheumatism, established in 1945, recommended early establishment of diagnostic and research centres in teaching and other major hospitals. To complement these centres of expertise, the Committee also wanted to see formal associations with peripheral clinics (to refer patients to the centres), and base hospitals (to accommodate long-stay patients). The Nuffield Trust was interested in this field, and was represented on the Sub-Committee by none other than John Stopford. He was able to bring the fruits of his labour back to Manchester and the Northwest – an archetypal industrial region.

Within twelve months of the Sub-Committee's recommendations, Stopford submitted a proposal to the Dean of the Manchester Medical School, requesting permission to negotiate with the Nuffield Foundation to build a diagnostic and research centre attached to the Manchester Royal Infirmary. He was keen to stress the 'social' as well as the scientific or academic aspects of medicine, along the lines suggested by the Goodenough Report. Co-operation with the University's new Department of Industrial Health would allow investigations of the social aspects, and the promotion of practical applications for the knowledge produced at the centre.

The rheumatism scheme was to have beds, laboratories and clinics at several sites around the region. Beds at the MRI would provide varied cases for teaching and research, while beds at the former municipal hospital at Withington focused on the treatment of patients suffering from rheumatoid arthritis. Outpatient clinics at Withington would specialize in therapeutic research, especially the provision of intra-articular injections. Chronic and semi-ambulatory cases would be sent out to the Devonshire Royal Hospital in the spa town of Buxton, as would patients in need of rehabilitation following treatment at the MRI or Withington (the Devonshire Royal had originated as a huge circular riding facility built for the Duke of Devonshire; in the late nineteenth century, it had been converted into a convalescent hospital for textile workers, and in 1948 it was taken over by the NHS). Laboratory and other specialist facilities were provided by the Infirmary and the University, including the departments of Physiotherapy, Pathology, Orthopaedics, and Industrial

Health. Thus the scheme worked on the basis of a functional region-alization: a highly organized collective of discrete institutions centred around a teaching hospital, devised to enable efficient and productive use of clinical material in teaching and research. Stopford and his friends were exploiting the openness of a national system supported by general taxation, in which many of the old barriers of ownership and need for payment had gone; regional planning for particular functions was now possible, though funding the research remained a challenge.

The Manchester Rheumatism scheme is a good example of how clinical research could be used to support a regional infrastructure of specialist services. With no central government money specifically set aside for NHS research, an ability to impress the University Grants Committee and to attract external sources of funding – such as grants from the Nuffield Foundation – was crucial to the success of the clinical research enterprise. As we have seen, post-war Manchester medicine was well connected, though more for clinical research than for basic medical sciences.

Group services and the UMH in the 1940s and 1950s

The health of the UMH in the uncertain 1950s was not entirely about clinical disciplines. We have noted the importance of service departments, and many of the gains of the early NHS came from the service specialisms such as pathology, radiology and anaesthetics for which full consultant posts were now available. Important too, was the better organization of non-medical supporting services such as estates management.

The Pharmacy Department of the UMH was one of the earliest departments to be reorganized on a group basis. The Department of Clinical Pathology was similarly reorganized in the early years to serve the whole of the UMH, building on its special role as part of the wartime Emergency Public Health Laboratory Service (a branch of the Emergency Medical Service). Diagnostic Radiology was another example of group work in action, but it proved complicated. To reduce loadings, some work was transferred from the Main X-Ray Department of the MRI to other UMH facilities, and some to hospitals outside the group, especially to the Christie cancer hospital. Neurosurgical radiology was carried out in the neurosurgical block, to integrate with clinical work. These divisions, however, together with gross overwork, made the Department rather difficult to run. The pressure increased further during the 1950s, when the Mass Miniature Radiography Unit was developed to screen for pulmonary tuberculosis, including compulsory annual checks on all hospital

staff. Other group departments included the Department of Physical Medicine, the Department of Venereal Diseases (through which the MRI shared staff and appointments with the Regional Hospital Board's St. Luke's Clinic in Salford), and the new Department of Anaesthetics, founded in 1947 when Dr H. J. Brennan was appointed Director. Manchester anaesthetists collaborated with ICI Pharmaceuticals in the development of Halothane – the first and most successful of a new generation of anaesthetics.

Under the new Board of Governors of the UMH, new group facilities were created during the late 1940s and early 1950s to service buildings on the whole site. In April 1949 for instance, a Central Works Committee began to oversee day-to-day maintenance work, minor alterations and future developments. Subsequently, a Clerk of Works (in charge of staff and administration), and a Group Architect and a Group Engineer (responsible for all Boiler, Heating and allied services), were appointed to run the new Works Department and to attempt economies of scale. For example, the window-cleaning bill for the Infirmary's 6,000 windows was reduced by organizing the service on a group basis and terminating agreements with outside contractors. Similar group reorganizations followed for Central Supplies, the Laundry, Boiler House services – and even, in 1950, for a new group Chaplain.

In addition to these new group services, interaction between staff and cross-referral of patients was also actively encouraged. Staff from the Manchester Dental and the Foot Hospital increasingly attended MRI outpatient and special clinics, partly to raise their professional profiles. But overall, the first years of the UMH were a time of continued independent identity and pride for the City's great hospitals.

The Bicentenary of the Infirmary

In July 1952, the Infirmary celebrated two hundred years of service with four days of commemorative events, and the publication of the *Portrait of a Hospital*, a history of the hospital by the MRI physician and historian, William Brockbank. A Service of Thanksgiving was held at the Manchester Cathedral, followed by a Civic lunch at the Town Hall, attended by representatives of all the hospital staff and the local dignitaries. There was also a ceremony in the Nurses' Great Hall to unveil special tablets which marked the anniversary in different ways: one symbolizing the opening of the first Infirmary in a house in the centre of the city in 1752; one to honour the continuance of the Infirmary as a place for the care of the sick; and one to mark the anniversary itself. The Minister of Health, Iain Macleod, presented badges and prizes to newly qualified nurses in the Nurses New Home, and was subsequently honoured with an evening banquet in the Great Hall. To complete the celebrations, several of the Infirmary's departments set up displays of new equipment and research projects. A great institution, honouring its local links, was moving forwards as part of a national network of practice, teaching and research.

Figure 9. Dr William Brockbank, Infirmary physician and author of the 1952 publication, Portrait of a Hospital.

CHAPTER THREE

New Structures and New Buildings, 1960–1974

B Y THE 1960s, technological advances in dialysis, transplantation, cardiac surgery, intensive care, and chemotherapies were offering hope in once hopeless cases. More mundanely, but no less formative of modern medicine, the 1960s was also a time of administrative renovation in the NHS. Rationalization, efficiency protocols and a new managerial structure were introduced to the United Manchester Hospitals. Although grouped together since the introduction of the National Health Service in 1948, it was not really until the 1960s that the United Manchester Hospitals truly cohered in terms of management and day-to-day practice. Individual hospitals accustomed to running their own affairs were amalgamated into one huge operation, employing thousands and sharing resources.

Other significant changes in the education of Manchester's doctors, nurses and technical staff were also underway. National directives to increase the numbers of undergraduates enrolling at medical schools, for instance, helped establish the case for the construction of the new Medical School building; and the pressure for more postgraduate and continuing training led to Postgraduate Centres in hospitals across the Region.

The 1960s was also a hopeful time in the planning of hospital services. Very few hospitals were built in Britain during the 1950s, even by the standards of the interwar decades, and development in Manchester was mostly at the city's former hospital for consumption at Baguley, which had undergone considerable expansion (in the form of rows of new hutted accommodation) as an Emergency Medical Service hospital. Following the war, the original sanatorium continued as a chest hospital, while the EMS huts became the germ of the Wythenshawe Hospital. A 1955 government survey listed Wythenshawe for rebuilding as a flagship NHS general hospital. But the first new building to be opened was ten years later

– the Maternity Unit, which was followed by accommodation for general medicine and general surgery, paediatrics, orthopaedics, ENT, dermatology and plastic surgery.

In the fifties, though the NHS had hugely improved staffing and services across Manchester and the rest of the country, the building of housing and schools had been prioritized over hospitals. Under Enoch Powell as Minister of Health, however, a new round of building schemes was called for, and the 1962 national *Hospital Plan* laid out proposals for many new hospitals and substantial upgrading of old ones. In the early sixties, the UMH expected to knock down their collection of Victorian and Edwardian buildings and to replace them with a high technology, integrated teaching-hospital.

But in fact the expansion of local clinical teaching largely took place beyond the central site. By a successful collaboration between the Department of Health and Social Security, the University Grants Committee, the Regional Health Authority, the University and the UMH administration, two new teaching hospitals were established for Manchester: the Teaching Hospitals of South Manchester (at Withington and the new Wythenshawe hospital), and the Salford Teaching Hospital Group (based at Hope Hospital).

Figure 10. By the early 1950s the MRI was in sore need of repair and new buildings. As can be seen in this aerial photograph, it occupied the same buildings as outlined in the Edwardian MRI floor-plan (see Figure 6) – except for the bomb-damage to the front buildings.

The National Hospital Plan and its implications for the UMH

The need for a physical refashioning of the national hospital service was urgent. The major remedy, outlined in the national *Hospital Plan*, was to be 'District General Hospitals' which could provide a full range of sub-regional specialties. £500 million was promised nationally, to build ninety hospitals and to remodel or refurbish more than a hundred others. These included both general and teaching hospitals, with the latter expected to provide district general services where appropriate, in addition to their special and regional services.

The Ministry's published recommendations generally followed the priorities for rebuilding and modernization which had been set out by the Committee of Management of the UMH, but there were also significant differences. The building of a new Maternity Hospital on the Oxford Road site adjacent to St. Mary's Gynaecological Hospital and the addition of a second floor to the Dental Hospital were approved after some revision and negotiation, but the Ministry was much less impressed with plans for the MRI, insisting that the Board of Governors of the UMH urgently appoint a planning architect to clarify the requests. The Ministry also turned down requests to build a further two-storey block for the Orthopaedic Department, for additional clinical research space, and to extend the much patched-up Main X-Ray Department. In each case they indicated that less expensive stop-gap measures would be considered (and they did, in fact, issue a special grant of £10,000 to cover cost of repairs to 1908 buildings at the MRI); but they stressed that no major requests would be considered until a proper large scale planning operation had been conducted and a site-plan approved by the Ministry.

By November 1962 the Governors of the UMH had organized a brief for a planning consultant, while continuing their own efforts to redevelop the Site. Major new building in this period included the new Nurses' Training School, opened in 1962 in a two-storey block adjacent to the Nurses' New Home. In 1963, a Sterile Products Laboratory was completed underneath the Pharmacy as part of a long-term attempt to reduce the MRI's soaring drugs bill. The major clinical development was the Metabolic, Rheumatism and Medical Illustration block opened in 1963, aided by a donation of £30,000 from the Wellcome Trust.

In addition to its role in research, training and the provision of regional specialist services, the new hospital was intended to function as a district hospital providing a full range of routine services for a population of 250,000. In response to the revised UMH planning report, the Ministry agreed to the building of a Paediatric Unit

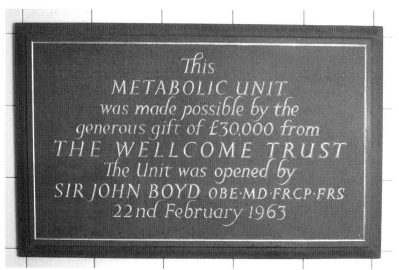

Figure 11. By the 1960s, some new specialty facilities were built. Grants and donations from private endowments and from biomedical charities such as the Wellcome Trust were crucial in a cash-strapped NHS.

(including an out-patients clinic) and a 50-bed Psychiatric Unit on the Oxford Road site. Plans to rebuild the UMH as a single integrated teaching hospital to replace the MRI, St. Mary's and the Eye Hospital were initially approved, but did not materialize. They were deferred by national cost-cutting, and abandoned in the 1970s.

Maternity services in Manchester: the building of a new hospital

In 1959 a banner headline in the *Manchester Evening News* proclaimed 'Women Who Weep At Hospital Door' – these were expectant mothers refused admission to St. Mary's because of the bed shortages. Overspill maternity facilities were provided at Withington, Baguley and Salford, but there was intense pressure for more maternity accommodation and for nursing and midwifery staff. To provide hospital confinements for about half of all births had been a priority in the 1962 *Hospital Plan*, and most towns received new maternity accommodation (at a time when the birth rate had begun to fall). In Manchester, plans were announced for a large new maternity hospital to be built on Hathersage Road, the east-side of the Oxford Road site. Work began in 1964, intended as the first step of a much wider project to completely rebuild the MRI, St. Mary's, the Eye Hospital and the Dental Hospital.

The new maternity service was officially opened by the Queen in June 1970, to enthusiastic national press attention. The steel and concrete 'match-box on a muffin' design was in keeping with architectural trends of the time. The restricted ground space available (amounting to a mere 2.5 acres) favoured building upwards, while the vertical communication between departments through a central system of elevators, and the central provision of supplies, laboratory services and X-rays were expected to increase efficiency and enhance working conditions. Geographic centralization of resources extended through to the delivery rooms, which were also located in the central tower block, so that babies were no longer delivered on the wards.

A new design for the hospital's antenatal clinic meant that patients moved through the various departments in an orderly clock-wise fashion, once again increasing efficiency. The outpatient department was similarly rationalized, with patients waiting directly outside the doors of consulting rooms, not in waiting rooms. It is little wonder that the *Manchester Evening News* reported the new hospital to be in: 'the kindest possible way …a "baby factory"'!

The 25-bed General Practitioner Unit, another significant innovation, was the result of negotiations between the UMH Board of Governors and the Local Health Authority. It was staffed by GPs and Local Health Authority domiciliary midwives. Women who were 'booked in' during the early months of pregnancy, or admitted as a result of late complications, could continue under the care of their own GP, whilst difficult deliveries could be carried out by a midwife, supported if necessary by the consultants and special clinical facilities close by. The Unit also allowed medical students to see GPs working

Figure 12. The old and the new St. Mary's buildings, side-by-side on Hathersage Road.

in smart, high-tech surroundings, helping to dispel perceptions of general practice as an unattractive career option.

The new hospital also contained a 'research floor' funded by the University; and every ward unit, central delivery unit and special care baby unit had research and teaching programmes built around them. Areas of special interest from the late 1960s included fertility research based on the synthetic sex hormone Clomiphene (a project begun in 1965 by Ian Morris), and work on diabetic pregnancies and subsequent infant fatalities. This latter research involved studies of the amniotic fluid, linking with work on foetal development more generally, and with studies on hormones and kidney disease. The new hospital was intended to allow unprecedented opportunities for integrated, multi-team clinical research, laboratory and animal work. Unfortunately, the original plans to provide functional flexibility by allowing substantial structural re-modelling were not realised, and the tower block became unpopular with both patients and staff. St. Mary's, however, continued to develop a range of specialist treatments. The laboratory for medical genetics and the associated genetic counselling service served as national models in the 1970s and 1980s, and as the basis for a later expansion in dysmorphology and molecular genetics.

Throughout the 1970s and beyond, the hospital continued to expand its facilities and services. The Abortion Act of 1967 led to a local working party, and to subsequent provision of a full range of abortion services by the early 1970s. Further links with the University were also established, for instance with the formation of a Department of Gynaecological Urology in 1971. Also in 1971, St. Mary's became one of the first UK maternity hospitals to form a neonatal 'flying squad' to transport critically ill babies to its neonatal intensive care and newly formed neonatal surgical unit. Like similar units established at the MRI, all of these new services at St. Mary's were regional, and in some cases national, centres.

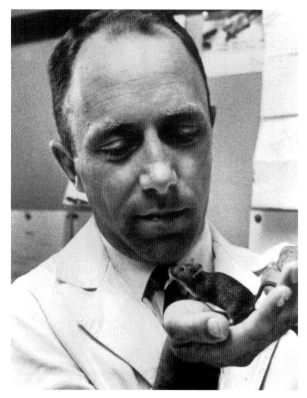

Figure 13. Alan Emery pioneered Medical Genetics at St. Mary's, and under Rodney Harris and Dian Donnai the department gained an international reputation.

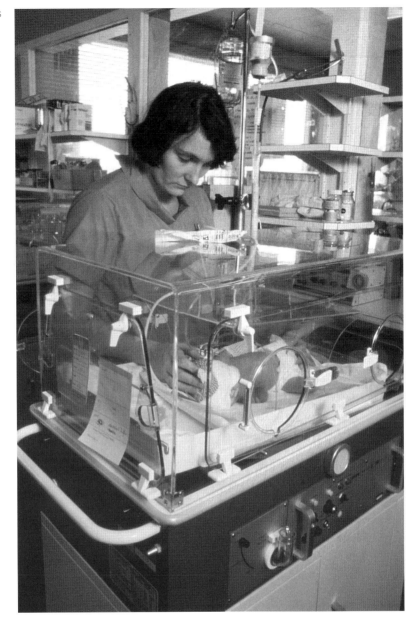

Figure 14. St. Mary's Hospital led the Northwest in the care of newborn babies. New services in the 1970s included this neonatal intensive care unit housed in the new medical tower.

Nursing and medical administration: Salmon and Cogwheel

The nursing profession changed greatly in the 1960s. A now retired nurse remembered: 'People went into nursing because it was a vocation. I didn't ask when I went [to my admissions interview] how much I would earn. It didn't *occur* to me to ask how much I would earn. One of the girls I started training with, who came for interview the same time as me, did ask what her salary was – and was in trouble! And Matron said to her, "Young lady, that is *not* important!" …So I didn't ask! It was quite a few months before I found out how much I earned!' A wise choice to remain silent, perhaps, and also a recognition of the need to have a 'calling'. Yet, though a culture that eschewed material reward was very much alive at the MRI in the 1960s, Infirmary nurses were also involved in protests over their historically low pay (once appropriate for, and intended for, respectable middle-class girls). MRI nurses, and a thousand other North West nurses, gathered outside Manchester town hall in April 1962 under the banner 'Angels with Empty Purses.'

Low pay wasn't the only source of discontent for nurses: low status and marginalization by medical management structures were also troubling. In 1961 Enoch Powell called together a national committee, mainly of senior nurses, under the Chairmanship of Brian Salmon, a businessman and administrator for Westminster Hospital, to advise on the reform of nursing structures. The Salmon Report of 1967 recommended a substantial reorganization of hospital nursing, and new roles for senior nurses within hospital management. A new system of 'grading' was to be introduced, mirroring a similar system on the administrative side; old job categories were to go, including (to the dismay of some!) the 'Matron'. Although generally welcomed by nurses, the report's recommendations were criticized by some doctors in Manchester as elsewhere who were concerned that giving more administrative responsibility to senior nurses would take nursing time from the wards – an issue that would resonate within the health service through to the present. Although the Salmon grading system and much else were changed in later NHS reorganizations, debate has continued over the roles of the nurse – as administrator, manager, expert, and provider of patient care.

The report's recommendations also included proposals to relieve nurses from their non-nursing duties, shifting this work to domestic staff. To prepare all such staff for their new responsibilities, a special UMH training scheme was arranged for November 1970, run by the three Domestic Superintendents – Mrs Sylvia Wellings from St. Mary's, Miss Elizabeth Ainsworth from the Infirmary, and Miss Susan Arch from the Eye Hospital. Senior staff members from the departments of Catering, Nursing Supplies and Nurse Teaching participated in the scheme, ensuring that staff knew the latest ideas in nursing and domestic care. The practical teaching included the correct use of equipment and materials, accident prevention, security and the maintenance of hygienic standards. Writing in the hospital journal *Telstar* in 1971, Wellings welcomed the changes and noted that: 'The staff now have a smart standard uniform which is worn throughout the Group and it is pleasing to see the Domestic Staff sharing the dining room and changing facilities with all grades in the Hospital.' Divisions of class and rank were slowly breaking down under the 'integrated' philosophy of the UMH.

In the same year as the Salmon Report, the Ministry also published two Cogwheel Reports on the organization of doctors in hospitals (named after the distinctive illustration on the front cover). The reports had emerged from a working party established in 1966 under the Chief Medical Officer, Sir George Godber, in response to calls for more managerial training for doctors and better organization of medical and surgical categories. The first Cogwheel Report recommended the introduction of 'clinical divisions': groupings of similar specialties for the purposes of administration. Representatives of each division would sit on a medical executive committee, so maintaining much closer links between the doctors and managers, and between the hospitals in a group. Adding representatives of local General Practice and of Regional Authorities would further bridge traditional divides between the different branches of the Health Service, so improving communication and co-ordination.

Both Salmon and Cogwheel reforms sought a new spirit of partnership between managers, doctors and nurses. Many of the old hierarchies of class and tradition crumbled during the 1960s – in the hospital, as in British society more generally.

Reorganization of the MRI and the UMH, 1968–1974

The first phase of administrative reorganization of the UMH followed many of the recommendations of the first Cogwheel Report. The Board of Governors outlined a rationalized structure intended to speed administrative change and the planning of new buildings. Some thirty separate hospital committees were replaced in the early summer of 1968 by five Group Committees – Finance and Establishment, Medical Executive, Nursing and Midwifery, General Services, and Patients' Services – each acting as a functional committee of the UMH Board of Governors. The following year saw the publication of the first combined hospital group report – *The United Manchester Hospitals Report and Year Book* – which replaced the single institution annual reports, and marked a significant step towards a group identity.

The new Medical Executive was to oversee ten clinical Divisions across the UMH: Medicine (including Psychiatry), Surgery, Obstetrics and Gynaecology, Paediatrics, Ophthalmology, Laboratory Medicine, Anaesthetics, Radiology, Dentistry, and Medical Education – all of which were represented on the Executive. Responsibility for clinical work and policy was vested in divisional staff, with the Executive managing financial matters, integrating policy across the divisions and reporting to the Board of Governors. To encourage integrated thinking, numerous interdivisional working groups were established, including nurses as well as doctors. Moreover, though medical membership of Divisions was restricted to consultant grades and senior registrars (and to University staff of similar status), nursing staff were brought into divisional administration on a level *equal* to consultant colleagues, so reflecting some of the key recommendations laid down in the first Salmon Report. The new structures were meant to encourage teamwork, with collective responsibility for resources; the consultants, especially, were expected to review their various needs before seeking funds from the lay administrators.

Restraint as a fact of life was vigorously promoted through the 'vigilance against waste' campaign in the pages of *Telstar* – the group hospital journal which was started in November 1969 and edited for most of its life (1969–1973) by Elizabeth Wilson, the UMH Public Relations Officer and Voluntary Services Coordinator. *Telstar* was intended to reflect these new styles of management and communication. Its name, taken from the communications satellite, was chosen through a competition with a £2 prize. Here it referred to two-way communication across more than 4,000 staff at all levels (Tel), and between all the five hospitals in the group (star).

The drive for 'efficiency' and 'participatory management' also produced various incentive schemes and productivity agreements for ancillary staff. Work Study Officers were assigned to assess the effectiveness of working practices within the hospital departments, and, if necessary, to suggest alterations and set bonus targets. The potential for disgruntlement was obvious, and *Telstar* was employed to ensure that information on the new schemes was reliable, and to reassure ancillary staff that incentive schemes did not imply laziness. Hence the motto: 'There is a great difference between working hard and working effectively'!

The UMH absorbed the administrative changes encouraged by Salmon and Cogwheel, and changed its functional structure, but with some 'accommodation'. Informal but long established working groups persisted alongside new official structures. Some staff were frustrated by these 'shadow committees', while others questioned the relevance of the new Divisional structures and working groups. Many clinicians were unwilling to act as administrators, seeing the new arrangements as a distraction from medical work: the burgeoning clinical administrator posts would take good doctors and nurses away from the wards. The ensuing debates about the relative roles of professional administrators and administering professionals have continued to the present, through an accelerating sequence of administrative disruptions.

The Stopford Building and the expansion of medical teaching

Figure 15. The new Manchester Medical School was opened in 1973, and named in honour of John Stopford (see figure 7). It was the largest building then funded by the national University Grants Committee, and much of the design was due to Dr Bill Beswick, the executive Dean of Medicine.

Enrolment in British medical schools declined alarmingly during the 1960s, and it became clear that urgent action was needed to ensure an adequate supply of doctors for the years ahead. Through the University Grants Committee, the government made funds available for the rebuilding and enlargement of existing medical schools and for the building of new ones. This provision met the aspirations of certain Manchester men who were keen to expand undergraduate medical education and increase the numbers of academic medical staff. The Manchester Medical School accepted its first increased intake in 1968, some five years before its new premises were opened (the former University Physics Department buildings absorbed the overflow in the meantime!). In 1973 the new Manchester Medical School building opened its doors, named in memory of Lord (John) Stopford of Fallowfield. The University was concerned to

keep up numbers, and when the clinical school at the University of St. Andrews announced its impending closure, several senior Manchester representatives, Bill Beswick chief amongst them, agreed to take 75 Scottish students each year for clinical studies.

The large increase in undergraduates put considerable pressure on clinical teaching resources in Manchester. The development of the University Hospital of South Manchester – comprising the Withington general hospital, the Christie cancer hospital and the Duchess of York Hospital for Babies – was speeded up to provide more clinical teaching placements. The majority of routine hospital work in South Manchester was undertaken at Withington, which also housed a major psychiatric facility, and a breast cancer service that operated closely with the Christie. The new Wythenshawe Hospital also became part of the group. During 1973 the MRI helped prepare Hope Hospital, Salford as the third undergraduate teaching hospital of the Manchester Medical School. In that year, the University appointed Leslie Turnberg to be Hope's Professor of Medicine, the first of four clinical professors appointed during the 1970s, under whom the new facility thrived.

More distant hospitals were also used for medical student residencies. By the early 1970s, roughly 40% of Manchester's clinical students spent their 4th year studying in a regional District General Hospital. Such moves were not only a response to pressure for more clinical places: many doctors felt that students should observe disease in an environment representative of community incidence. In other words, they should spend time away from the highly selective patient–intakes and the increasing specialisation of the teaching hospitals.

The Manchester Royal Eye Hospital: a rising star of the group

When the MRI moved to Oxford Road in the early twentieth century, it bought up the land around the (already resident) Manchester Royal Eye Hospital. An agreement was soon reached, however, that the Eye Hospital could make reasonable purchase and use of Infirmary land on condition that it took in all of its neighbour's inpatient eye cases, and helped to train medical students. Taking advantage of this arrangement in 1939, the hospital built a new outpatients department on Nelson Street, which grew to be one of the busiest in the country. During the war, the Eye Hospital suffered many of the same building shortages and deprivations as the Infirmary; direct bomb–hits fatally wounded two members of staff.

The opportunity to become a teaching centre in conjunction with the MRI was welcomed by the Eye Hospital's Board of Management,

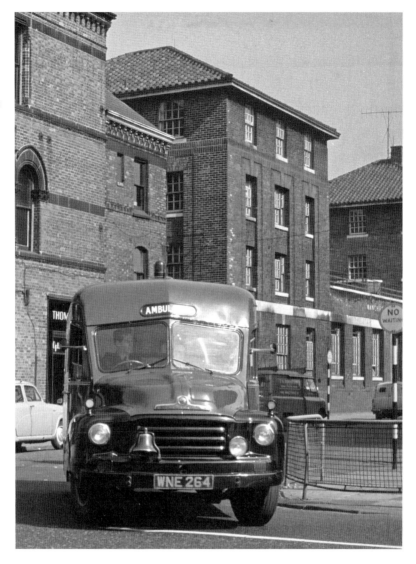

and its status as a regional teaching hospital was consolidated a
decade later with the inclusion of the Eye Hospital in the UMH
group. Links were also forged with the University Department of
Ophthalmology, stimulating research work at the hospital during the
1950s. In 1965 an Orthoptic Training School was opened, and links
were strengthened with the Department of Ophthalmic Optics at
the University of Manchester Institute of Science and Technology
(UMIST). The Eye Hospital soon grew to be the largest ophthalmic
teaching institution in the North of England, and by the 1960s some
fifty of the approximately three hundred consultants working across
the country had done their training at the hospital.

In the 1960s the Eye Hospital launched a major community out-reach venture – to establish and maintain an 'eye bank' for corneal grafting. Backed by the local press, hospital and local authority staff worked with the Royal National Institute for the Blind to promote the surgical work of the hospital and overcome public squeamishness about eye donation. The high success rates of this restorative surgery seemed to be convincing, and by 1965 the hospital (helped by the MRI) had enrolled some 6,000 volunteer donors into its scheme. Many more were needed, however, at a time when only patients who had gone completely blind had any hope of getting onto the waiting list. Great energy was put into recruitment, and into educating the public of the need to inform the hospital quickly if their registered family member died (the eyes quickly became unusable if not frozen shortly after death). Such endeavours are ongoing as the range of conditions treated through the Manchester Eye Bank expands and the need for donors continues to increase.

The Manchester Foot Hospital and the University Dental Hospital

From its humble beginnings in the 1920s, the Manchester Foot Hospital had been organized as a teaching clinic, and its various departments had received the support and advice of MRI and University staff. By the 1960s, one department in particular had grown substantially in size and prominence: in 1961 the chiropodial appliance department opened new purpose-built premises, costing £15,000 and intended specifically for student training. It was one of the first such facilities in the country. Sir Harry Platt, the University's Professor of Orthopaedic Surgery and a long-time supporter of the hospital, officiated at the opening ceremonies.

In 1969 the expanded Manchester Foot Hospital School of Chiropody merged with the Salford College of Technology School of Chiropody to become the new Northern College of Chiropody. It taught a three-year, full-time curriculum as laid down by the Chiropodists Board of the Council for Professions Supplementary to Medicine (the body dealing with State registration of chiropodists).

The long-awaited redevelopment of the University Dental Hospital of Manchester was finally completed in the early months of 1972. The clinical workload of the Hospital had continued to increase sharply, especially in primary care and oral surgery, and the new facilities were also intended to enhance relationships between the Dental Hospital, the University and other local teaching hospitals. New facilities, a new curriculum and new visiting arrangements with City dental clinics were all intended to raise the profile of

Manchester as a centre of excellence in dental teaching, and the 1970s did indeed see a steady rise in student enrolment. The re-equipped dental hospital also provided better training for dental technicians (building on the introduction of technician qualifications in the mid-1960s), and of dental surgery assistants and other ancillary staff. Finally, in keeping with clinical trends evident across medicine and surgery, the Dental Hospital began an extensive programme of postgraduate training and practitioner 'refresher' courses conducted through a University postgraduate advisor in dental education, linked to similar professionals across the Northwest.

Nursing education in the UMH and the University of Manchester

The first nursing diploma to be introduced by the University of Manchester was in Community Nursing, offered through the Department of Social and Preventative Medicine from 1959. In 1969 the diploma was 'upgraded' to a bachelor's degree and the graduates were then entitled to apply to the General Nursing Council for Registration as nurses. Initially, the undergraduate nurses gained their practical instruction at the Crumpsall Hospital in north Manchester, but after the introduction of the General Nursing Council Syllabus to the UMH in January 1971, University nursing students started to be offered placements at MRI. In 1973 a Department of Nursing was established as part of the University's Faculty of Medicine, and a year later Jean McFarlane was appointed as England's first Professor of Nursing. The School not only consolidated the new degree programme, it also underscored new trends in postgraduate nursing education: the early 1970s saw several nurses register for advanced degrees (both MSc and PhD) in the Faculty of Medicine, and the School introduced a Diploma in Advanced Nursing Studies to increase access to higher education amongst the profession. These initiatives were advanced with enthusiasm and greeted with both delight and disdain.

Research and specialty services across the UMH

During the 1960s, clinical research continued to be pursued vigorously in the MRI and across the UMH. Most of this research was carried out by doctors, but increasingly they were joined by biochemists, pharmacists, geneticists and other scientists, and by administrators, nurses and ancillary staff. As in earlier decades, research funds came from the University of Manchester and the hospitals' endowment funds, as well as from industrial sources (especially from Searle and from Geigy) and national bodies such as the Medical Research Council and the Department of Health. New collaborations involved numerous staff in Regional Hospital Board hospitals.

On the national scene, Douglas Black, the renal physician and Manchester's Professor of Medicine, was called to become the Department of Health's Chief Scientific Officer in 1974, as part of the fallout from the Rothschild Report on Medical Research. This report had suggested the formation of an executive department, headed by the new post of Chief Scientist, to help make research more productive and 'practically' relevant. Throughout his time in the post, Black struggled to encourage a more nuanced view of the benefits of clinical research and to forge a new style of relationship between the Department of Health and the Medical Research Council.

The MRI continued to house five Medical Units and five Surgical Units, but as we have noted, there was an increasing range of other specialty and sub-specialty departments and units. Post-war departments of Rheumatology, Social and Preventative Medicine, Occupational Health, Physical Medicine, Dermatology, Venerology, and Neurology, and sub-departments of Cardiology and Clinical Haematology, were joined by departments of Anaesthetics, Child Health, Medical Physics, and Medical Genetics, most of which had been split off from the Department of Medicine. A new special unit for Renal Transplantation shared a tissue-typing facility with the Medical Genetics Department, in the Pathology Laboratories of the new St. Mary's Maternity Hospital; and there were new Units for Metabolic Medicine and for Intensive/Coronary Care. Further specialist staff appointments were made in Urology, Thoracic and Cardiac Surgery, Audiology, Plastic Surgery, Human Serology, Cytology, Neuropathology, Obstetrical and Gynaecological Pathology, Pathology in relation to Rheumatology, Immunology, and Medical Physics. All were evidence of the rapid increase in medical science and specialization facilitated by the NHS and increased funding for Universities.

The new clinical Units were expected to advance patient care by concentrating the expertise of clinicians, service specialists, doctors, nurses and technicians – as in the three intensive-care units completed in 1969 for renal, coronary and respiratory care. A new Coronary Care Unit was constructed in the southern half of one of the male medical wards (the new Respiratory Unit took up the northern half). The six coronary beds were overlooked by a central Nurses' Station, which also received information from bedside monitoring equipment (state-of-the-art computers for this purpose were provided for through donations from Ferranti Ltd). Senior nurses were trained in the interpretation of electrocardiograms, and in resuscitation and therapeutic methods, while a special medical Registrar, with duties in intensive care, provided additional clinical support. For any patient admitted to hospital after a heart attack, the risk of death peaked within the first few hours, but those who could be whisked straight to a Coronary Care Unit for the latest drugs and techniques tended to fare much better. The Coronary Care and Respiratory Intensive Care Units, although functioning independently, formed a Unitary Intensive Care Area, centralizing expensive monitoring equipment and staff expertise. Co-operation was to the fore. Opening the new Cardiac Surgery Unit in 1971, Sir Thomas Holmes Sellors, the President of the Royal College of Surgeons, suggested that: 'The days of the Prima Donna in the Theatre, when the Consultant held the stage surrounded only by an Anaesthetist, Nurse and a junior Doctor, are now behind us. Today techniques are now more specialized and *all* those treating the patient work as a team.'

Opened on 31 October 1969, the Renal Unit occupied the ground floor of one of the wings of the Private Patients' Home and contained eight transplant rooms, all of which were also equipped for dialysis treatment. As a joint project between the UMH and the Regional Hospital Board, it was meant to serve the whole of the Manchester region. In the previous year, as part of this regional

Figure 17. The MRI Renal Unit, opened in 1969, was one of several services headquartered within the United Manchester Hospitals but serving the medical needs of much of the Northwest.

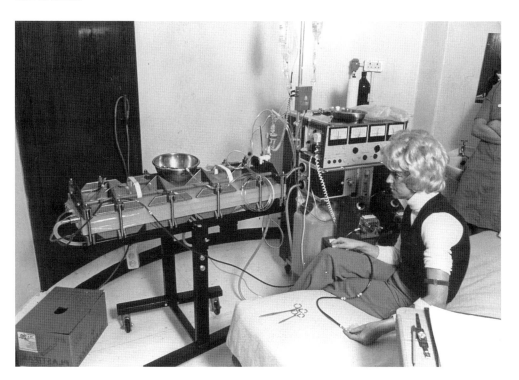

plan, the MRI renal team had developed the first of its 'satellite' units, establishing a dialysis unit at the Withington Hospital, so freeing the MRI unit for transplant work. Pioneered by the surgeon William Orr, and developed in the 1970s by the surgeon Robert Johnson and the physician Nettar Mallick, the Manchester transplant team gained an international reputation both for its survival rates amongst transplanted patients and for the sheer numbers of patients it eventually treated. However, as the Ward-Sister, Linda Whitworth, remembered, the transplant list took some time to build up. In the meantime, keen to keep up their special skills, the team also took in dialysis patients.

The 'team' structure nurtured in special units came to be widely copied. Speaking of the Renal Unit, Professor Mallick has recently commented that: 'Because of the way in which renal medicine developed, particularly in Britain, with relatively few doctors and quite a lot of nurses who were getting fed up with the bedpan routine – put it that way – we attracted from the beginning some very keen and dynamic nurses, some of the best nurses in the place; the ones wanting to go somewhere and do something new came to us because we were then at the cutting edge of anything in health. Dialysis and transplantation were *it* really …so we had a lot of good nurses! And being like that, they did not take very kindly to being told everything that they should do, nor could you afford to do it, because you had to rely on them as a team! So we developed the concept of the integrated team, literally years ahead of anybody, with one exception which was Intensive Care.'

In other areas of hospital life too, greater centralization of resources was evident. In 1969, for instance, George Hicks was appointed Central Administrative Officer in Charge of Group Portering Services, with a mandate to pool, standardize and train porters across the group. In these post-Cogwheel times, Hicks also headed a new Working Party drawn up from members of the portering staff of the UMH to advise on future improvements to services. In 1971 the 'Group Pathology' laboratories were opened, uniting a range of chemical pathology and haematology services; so too the Central Sterile Supply Department of 1971, which drew together several independent departments (some with quite distinct working practices) to manage an instrument through-put of some 30,000 individual pieces per day! The new building was attached to the Pharmacy Department, which over 20 years had changed radically. In the early years of the NHS the pharmacist, Mr J. B. Lloyd, had run a one-room dispensary mostly providing medicines to be taken by mouth; in 1971, this was but one room in a complex of laboratories which also prepared drugs for injection, plus ever growing volumes of sterile fluids, especially the dialysing fluid for the Kidney Unit, which had previously been prepared by the nursing staff on the wards.

The MRI was also home to Britain's first '5-Day Ward', an experimental venture launched in 1969, intended to increase the efficiency of intensive clinical investigations whilst reducing the inconvenience to the patient and the pressure on nursing resources. Patients requiring an intensive series of clinical tests were admitted in the week and would return home by Friday evening; most could take care of themselves, so the nursing staff could take time to explain the tests and develop their own expertise in the test techniques. Many of the patients had been in and out of hospital many times over long periods, occupying beds in normal wards, but often with little idea of what might be wrong. Speaking to the *Daily Mail* in 1971, when supermarkets were beginning to appear, Dr Longson called the new ward a 'Tesco affair'; whilst his nursing colleague, Sister Young, commented: 'A lot of time is spent talking to the patients, explaining things just to make sure they really understand and are not worrying secretly …Some may at first be frightened or bewildered – particularly the older people who find it difficult to adjust to a ward where patients sit around the fire chatting, pop out to the shops or to dinner with their husbands and only get into bed at night'!

A further well-publicised development involved Britain's first commercial CT scanner. EMI, the record company which had prospered from the Beatles, had supported one of their researchers, Godfrey Hounsfield, to develop his idea for computed tomography. Ian Isherwood, head of radiology at the MRI, met Hounsfield in February 1972 and with the backing of the DHSS secured one of the three machines which followed the prototype. Not without difficulty, it was installed in a new extension of the Neuroradiology Department, and the first patient was scanned in July 1973.

Public donations and the UMH

With the introduction of state-financed health care, public donations to the nation's hospitals declined; but the UMH continued to benefit from public fundraising and bequests, and the new high-technology specialist services proved popular targets for charity – or was it potential self–help? In the late 1960s, the Manchester Heart Aid Committee was set up by several Manchester businessmen to help purchase equipment for established cardiac surgery units. The Infirmary was the first hospital to benefit; a mobile plethysmocardiagraph, received in January 1971, enabled patients to be monitored during transit between the Intensive Care Unit and Theatre.

Nevertheless, dwindling public contributions meant dwindling endowment funds, and this was becoming a problem for the United Manchester Hospitals as they tried to keep pace with the latest developments in clinical research. As the group research report stated in 1969–1970: 'There is a mistaken belief that State funds are a cornucopia and that we have ample endowments …Our need for more voluntary support from the Manchester region is, therefore, urgent.'

In 1971, the MRI opened the Jefferson Library using donations in memory of the neurosurgeon Sir Geoffrey Jefferson. Today the Library is to be found in the MRI's Postgraduate Centre, but it began its life in the former 'Matron's flat' above the Medical Board Room. In accordance with Sir Geoffrey's wishes, it provided a quiet space in which to think and meditate, away from the bustle of the wards. The Jefferson Memorial Library Trustees – Dr F.R. Ferguson, Mr R.T. Johnson, V.F. Lambert and Lord (Robert) Platt – had raised funds for seven years in order to create the library, and the UMH Board of Governors agreed to pay for structural costs, librarians and an annual book grant. The Library, used especially by residents and junior hospital staff, was formally opened on 9 June 1971 by Sir Geoffrey's old friend and colleague, Sir Harry Platt.

Another honorific ceremony took place in December that year, when the nurses' homes, new and old, were renamed Sparshott House and Cobbett House, respectively. Miss Sparshott, a former MRI Matron, was honoured for her service and for raising funds to construct the Great Hall; while the lawyer Sir Walter Cobbett was honoured as a long-serving Chair of the MRI Management Committee, and for his substantial fundraising and his legal advice to the institution.

CHAPTER FOUR

The MRI within a Reorganized NHS, 1974–1990

O N 1 APRIL 1974, the country's hospital and specialty services, local authority health services and family practitioner services all merged into a single, unified 'Integrated Health Care' system. The concept of 'integration' was crucial: it guided efforts to reform statutory bodies and the structure of NHS management, but it also spoke of a much larger effort to re-educate public and medical professionals about the place and purpose of medicine and the health services. Whereas for many, *hospital* services were the basis and measure of health provision, the 1974 reorganization sought to create a more nuanced view that recognized the key role of curative medicine, but also stressed environmental health and health education. The reorganization was also designed to improve management; and for the first time a firm of management consultants helped design the new arrangements. The emphasis was on teams.

The 1974 reorganization attempted to remedy long-standing problems of communication and co-ordination between the three sections of the NHS: the hospitals, community services and general practice. From the 1950s, for example, there had been difficulties in transferring patients from hospital beds to residential accommodation run by the social services; and GPs were not represented on the authorities that ran hospitals. In future, the fourteen regional health authorities were to plan across all branches of the health service, and, through the creation of local joint consultative committees, they would liaise with the local government authorities, which remained responsible for environmental health and social services. This would be all the easier because the simultaneous reorganization of local government ensured that the new health 'Areas' corresponded to the new counties or metropolitan authorities.

Area Health Authorities themselves became directly responsible for a variety of health services transferred from local government, including family planning, school health, vaccinations, health centres, health visiting and home nursing.

Some of the area functions, including the running of hospitals, were devolved to district level. The Manchester Area Health Authority, which covered the same area as the City of Manchester, comprised three districts –– North, South and Central. In terms of hospitals, the first two more or less corresponded to the Hospital Management Committees of North Manchester and South Manchester; the third corresponded to the United Manchester Hospitals – the central teaching hospitals which were now included in the main NHS structure, rather than reporting directly to central government.

At district level, the service was to be run by managers, with no representatives of the public as owners of the service. Indeed, 'public representation' was coming to mean 'consumer representation', for which Community Health Councils (CHCs) were set up for each of the districts. These had no management powers, but typically drew their members from a range of local authorities, voluntary organizations and other local community groups; they were intended to bring the popular voice into two-way exchange with health service managers. Some Community Health Councils, especially in inner city areas, were openly critical of NHS provision, organization and management.

Many teaching hospitals did not like losing their special independent status, which had been enshrined within the original NHS legislation. Recognizing this, the DHSS consultative document issued in 1971 had undertaken that where there were substantial responsibilities for medical and dental clinical teaching, special arrangements would be made: 'to enable teaching hospitals to play a fully integrated role in the reorganized Health Service – to the benefit of all the Health Services in the districts in which they are situated – while retaining their individual identity and historic traditions and maintaining the special services they provide.' It was hoped that these special arrangements and services for 'Teaching Areas' would extend beyond the needs of undergraduate and postgraduate teaching, enabling teaching hospitals to develop their regional services and promote national and international standards for clinical practice, teaching, research and management.

From 1974, therefore, the United Manchester Hospitals grouping – the MRI (including Barnes Hospital), Royal Eye Hospital, St. Mary's Hospital, University Dental Hospital and the Foot Hospital – were now joined with St Luke's Clinic on Duke Street (home of the Venereology Unit), and with Community Health Services which had formerly been part of the Manchester Local Authority Health Services. These included the clinics and health centres located within the municipal wards of Ardwick, Gorton North, Gorton South, Hulme, Levenshulme, Lloyd Street, Longsight, Moss Side and Rusholme. This whole collection of hospitals and clinics were the responsibility of the new Manchester Area Health Authority (Teaching) Central District, one of the three districts of the Manchester Area Health Authority, which in turn was one of eleven areas under the North Western Regional Health Authority.

The Manchester Area Health Authority (Teaching) included representatives appointed by the Secretary of State, the Regional Health Authority, the University and the City of Manchester (County Councillors), and was assisted by four Area Team Managers (an Administrator, a Treasurer, and a Nursing and Medical Officer), three Area Senior Officers (Area Works Officer, Area Dental Officer and Area Pharmaceutical Officer) and District Managers. The Central District was run by a District Management Team directly responsible to the Area Health Authority, comprising two medical representatives (one consultant and one GP), a District Community Physician, a District Nursing Officer, a District Treasurer and a District Administrator. The sheer size of the new Central District made effective communication between its 4000 employees a daunting task. A first step was the production of a Staff Handbook for all members, and of a dedicated new journal *Central Issues*, that replaced the defunct *Telstar* and vigorously promoted a comprehensive news and information agenda.

This restructuring of the NHS was quickly recognized as seriously defective. The insertion of Areas between Region and Districts had created huge overlaps and uncertainties. Financial and staff cut-backs added to the difficulties. The system of consensus management that was supposed to integrate the perspectives of managers and professionals, seemed to many both time-consuming and frustrating.

When the Conservatives won back power in the 1979 election, NHS reform was again on the agenda. Spurred on by the findings of a Royal Commission Report on the management of NHS resources, the government embarked on ambitious plans to bring a new culture of managerialism to the health services. This philosophy would be promoted through performance and quality assessments, and by the refinement of information processing and transfer. It was intended to remove some of the more wasteful aspects of an older administrative style (and it took twenty years before government would begin to publicly recognize the inefficiencies *created* by such means). In a consultative paper, *Patients First*, published several months after they came to power, the government outlined proposals to remove the

Area tier and create District Health Authorities to make decisions at a more local level. Regional Authorities would offer guidance, but with a 'hands-off' approach to management at district level.

The consultations arising from *Patients First* culminated in a second reorganization of the NHS, in 1982, which stressed devolution of power. But measures were already being developed to increase central oversight, and in 1983 the Griffiths Report, by the managing director of Sainsbury's, called for a general management structure throughout the NHS. Hospitals were to have general managers who would be responsible for the implementation of national policy. The consequent replacement of the consensus model with a less inclusive form of management had a very mixed reception. Although the speed of decision-making was increased, the lack of transparency and issues of representation became key areas of concern and objection.

Critics of the Conservative government in the 1980s saw the NHS as particularly vulnerable. Concern was rife that the organization might eventually be dismantled to be replaced by private medical and insurance services, and indeed the 1980s was a period of significant expansion in private hospital provision (prompted, be it noted, by Barbara Castle as Secretary of State in the previous Labour government, who had attempted to reduce private practice within NHS hospitals). In the leafy Manchester suburb of Cheadle, a large new private hospital, the Alexandra Hospital, was opened in 1981. Financed by American Medical International (Europe) Ltd., it was targeted at those 200,000 individuals among the four million North West residents, who carried private health insurance. The Director of the Hospital, Mr John Jackson, was optimistic about future relationships between the Alexandra and the city's NHS hospitals, especially about reducing waiting lists and providing placements for post-registration medical officers (posts then under freeze at the MRI and other hospitals). Others, however, continued to see such facilities as a threat to the future of the NHS.

At the end of the 1980s, most regional health authorities were heavily in debt and were having to close beds. More patients were being treated, but waiting lists continued to grow, causing much resentment and discontent amongst the public and the health care professions. By the end of the decade, a third extensive reorganization of the NHS was already under consideration.

Financial difficulty: the MRI under pressure

The work of the Central District in the 1970s was handicapped both by a very unfavourable national economic climate and by major local problems such as the crumbling 1908 ward blocks. We have

seen that the dilapidated state of numerous MRI buildings had led
to Ministry of Health approval for a new integrated hospital to be
built on the Oxford Road site. But in 1975, the plans were finally
abandoned on grounds of cost, and a new report was commissioned
to urgently launch a new strategy. The 1977 Structural Engineers
Report recommended a less ambitious rebuilding for the MRI;
it also highlighted the pressing need (from government as well as
locally) to prioritize under-funded specialties such as geriatrics,
mental illness and children's services. With major redevelopment out
of the question, the Regional Health Authority urged the Districts
to plan a 'nucleus hospital' – working incrementally towards a core of
central services surrounded by blocks for particular specialisms.

Even modest capital expenditure could significantly improve
services, and ward refurbishment work was ongoing. In 1974, for

instance, one of the Infirmary wards was renewed as the hospital's first 'Adolescent Ward', with a schoolroom and games facilities. Like other contemporary ward refurbishments, the Adolescent Ward abandoned the 'Nightingale' organization of beds down both sides of one long room, and instead deployed a bays and cubicles arrangement. Although popular with patients (who gained considerably more privacy in the new layout), such wards presented extra challenges to nurses who could no longer keep an eye on all their charges.

In 1977 the three-storey Medical Ward Block was closed so that the roof could be replaced and the interior thoroughly repaired. During this period of modest up-grade, patients were decanted to beds in the Private Patients' Home (freed up following government-imposed restrictions on the use of pay-beds in NHS hospitals), and to an empty ward in St. Mary's. The decanting procedure was greatly facilitated by the completion of a long-planned linking corridor between the MRI and St. Mary's – to keep you dry on trips between the hospitals! In the next year, repairs were started on the non-clinical 1908 structures most in need of attention, specifically Cobbett House Nurses' Home and the Main Administrative Block, which included the Inpatient Admissions Office and doctors' residence, all of which required further elaborate decanting measures!

The following year work started on a project to rebuild the Surgical Block, including a new Outpatients department. National trends towards increased specialization in Emergency Medicine encouraged an extensive redevelopment of the Accident and Emergency Department within this new block, and the appointment of an A&E Consultant. Considerable effort was also made to improve teaching facilities, particularly for undergraduate medical students. The original 1908 clinical lecture theatre was radically upgraded and re-equipped, and a new small lecture theatre was built on the medical corridor, along with five new seminar rooms.

The upgrading of the Barnes Convalescent Hospital at Cheadle was part of plans to improve services for the elderly and for patients undergoing rehabilitation. In 1977, part of Barnes Hospital became the MRI's Continuation Hospital, containing a new 112-bedded Geriatric Unit with rehabilitation facilities; Barnes's existing 80 continuation beds were also refurbished. These developments were complemented on the Oxford Road site by the conversion of an 18-bed ward into a Geriatric Assessment Unit (within the MRI's newly re-roofed Medical Ward Block), and the appointment to the Infirmary of the District's first consultant geriatrician.

The MRI's long-established pharmaceutical laboratory was also further redeveloped in the late 1970s and, with a similar facility at North Manchester General Hospital, took on additional responsibilities for manufacturing drugs for hospitals across the Area. In 1977 a Clinical Pharmacy training programme was implemented as a joint venture between the Infirmary and the University. As the Area Health Authority Report for the year stated, it was expected to: 'develop pharmacists more able to contribute to the safe and effective use of drugs, and, in association with medical expenditure committees already in existence, improve the monitoring and control of expenditure on drugs'.

Money was extremely tight during the 1970s, especially after the global economic crisis of 1974. The pressure to cut expenditure led to a rethink of Area Health Authority policy on the use of hospital resources. Strategies to replace hospital services with cheaper, community-based alternatives included the development of short-stay and early discharge programmes. The integrated structure of the new NHS facilitated such strategies, but they put considerable strain on existing community services, such as District Nursing, and they led to tensions between service providers.

Another worry was the continued use of Central District hospital facilities by patients from outside the area. Although mechanisms were in place to compensate the MRI for the treatment of patients necessarily referred for very specialist services, there was no such provision in cases where treatments were also available in the patient's own district. Yet, many GPs preferred to send their patients to MRI departments that were widely regarded as 'centres of excellence' (Orthopaedics and Neurosurgery, particularly), and any restriction of this freedom of choice was obviously a sensitive matter.

During the 1970s and 1980s, the UMH institutions became increasingly 'sub-specialized'. For example, from the early 1970s, the Regional Angiography Service in Manchester Royal Eye Hospital attracted referrals from all over the North of England, as well as a stream of international professional visitors, enhancing the reputation of the hospital but also putting considerable strain on already stretched resources.

Work and play at the MRI in the 1970s

The opening of a new purpose-built crèche in 1971, under the care of Mrs Dawson, greatly affected the lives of many female staff members in the MRI. Nursing staff in particular were very enthusiastic about the new facility, and pressure for places was so great that work on an extension began in 1975. In other ways too, the Infirmary and the District sought to encourage working mothers. One particularly good example was the setting up of a 'Nursing Bank', an agency run by Elizabeth Bateson to employ ex-nurses, many of whom had

Figure 19. By the 1970s, the social and class distinctions of the old Infirmary were weakening, with more relaxed attitudes towards work and play.

left the service to marry and raise a family. This meant that nurses who could spare some time either day or night could come onto the wards without committing to regular working hours. Frances Roberts, the Nursing Careers Advisor, was a key figure in this innovation, as she was in the related 'Keep in Touch' initiative, which offered evening classes aimed especially at married women who had left the service to raise a family. In this way, many nurses were able to return to the profession on terms they could more easily reconcile with their family commitments.

As well as finding flexible ways of working, the Infirmary also helped staff to play. A United Manchester Hospitals Sports and Social Club had existed for a number of years before it was formally recognized by the UMH management in the late 1960s. Although some doctors felt such organizations to be unnecessary and inappropriate, from 1974 the Club was housed in the Nelson Street Lodge and equipped with a fully licensed bar.

Another club set up by ancillary staff in 1974 was officially recognized from the outset: a gathering of more than 100 MRI staff, present and retired, all with more than 25 years service, met at a luncheon on 17 December to inaugurate the 'Quarter Century Club'. Its purpose was to promote links and improve communication amongst the growing numbers of health service workers; and at a time when job-mobility was increasing, it recognized the long and dedicated service of so many MRI staff members. Indeed, an amusing entry in the inaugural edition of *Central Issues* noted that when nine members of staff in the Group Supplies Department had added up their years of service to the MRI, they were startled to find that it amounted to 258 years! Although an 'Old Residents Club' had existed for doctors since 1908, the Sports and Social Club and the Quarter of a Century Club were the first social organizations open to all staff. They were hugely successful, and included many Infirmary doctors.

The status and formal organization of non-clinical staff in the MRI also changed in other ways. In 1974, for instance, the MRI hosted the Annual General Meeting of the National Association of Hospital Head Porters. It was the first such meeting to be held in the North of England, and arose from an article published in the *British Hospital Journal* on the desirability of middle management training for Head Porters in large hospitals, written by three north western Head Porters, Mr S. Jolley of Leigh Infirmary, Mr W. J. McManus of Withington Hospital and Mr R. Nuttall of Manchester Royal Infirmary. In 1975 the MRI saw another first when separate rates of pay for female ancillary staff were abolished and all staff were awarded equal pay for equivalent work. Though the equality was welcomed, the rates themselves were not. The 1970s and early 1980s saw much industrial unrest as government struggled to control inflation and public sector pay – in the face of strong unions and furious health service staff.

Industrial unrest

For the first twenty years of its existence, the National Health Service had been relatively free of serious industrial unrest, but in the 1970s and early 1980s, a series of national strikes and work-to-rule campaigns caused major headaches for government and local adminis-trators. There were, however, numerous industrial-relations successes at the local level. The 1974 reorganization had required a further integration and rationalization of group resources, including the integration of hospital switchboards. Staff accustomed to autonomy within relatively independent hospitals did not immediately welcome the idea, but as one telecommunications worker, Mike Carey, remembers: 'It went quite well, because George [Hicks], who was my supervisor at the time was running it … and because he did such a good job of it there was no industrial relations problems whatsoever! There were one or two problems about wages, but no industrial relations problems …it was handled very well!' Despite the introduction of the Area tier, older ideas of hospital organization remained: for telecommunications, for instance, the old acronym

'UMH' remained in common use – but from 1974 it was said to stand for 'Under Mr Hicks'!

Pay was a national issue, as was long hours, and through the 1980s junior doctors and nurses in particular, frequently mounted demonstrations against the government and 'worked to rule' within the District service. There was also much professional dissatisfaction with the way the health service provided care to patients. The reputation of the NHS was certainly suffering but, as is nicely shown by the case of the new Manchester Diabetes Centre, some deficiencies in health care provision could be remedied within existing structures, for the benefit of all.

The MRI and community access: the Manchester Diabetes Centre

In 1989 Stephen Tomlinson, the University's Professor of Medicine at the MRI, established a new service, the Manchester Diabetes Centre, on Hathersage Road, at the southern edge of the Oxford Road site. Lack of space within the Infirmary was not the only reason why Tomlinson sought to establish the clinic outside the hospital. He: 'thought it important to be slightly distanced from the hospital. To engage *directly* with the people who have the problems.' The name of the facility – the *Manchester* Diabetes Centre (MDC) – made no mention of the hospital; it was intended to suggest the availability of care for all. Patients needed an initial GP referral to the Centre, but they were then able to access all its services (including specialist clinics) on demand – a radical departure from the old Diabetes Clinic, and, more generally, from the customary operation of NHS services.

In the local medical students' journal *Mediscope* in February 1988, Tomlinson criticized existing practice: 'How do we currently provide education? In a busy district general hospital (or a teaching hospital) the traditional diabetic clinic is held once or twice a week. A single consultant, with perhaps clinical assistants and a [Senior House Officer] might be expected to see well over a hundred patients in a three-hour session. People wait for periods of up to four-hours to see a doctor for five minutes or even less. It is quite likely that they will see a different doctor each time they come. Such an environment is not conducive to education!' Effective patient education and increased standards of self-care would, he argued, only come about if medical professionals *and patients* altered their views of what diabetes care ought to be, and who ought to participate in it. He continued: 'In surveys done at the MRI, knowledge-scores amongst patients have been found to be appallingly low. People have little idea *why* they attend the clinic. Their major anxieties revolve around such issues as missing their turn, and yet despite all this, when asked whether they are satisfied with the medical services provided, over two-thirds are satisfied or very satisfied. Thus, knowledge is poor and expectations are low … The solution lies in teamwork with its objective being *prevention* and *self care* through education. One way of promoting this philosophy is to abandon the traditional diabetic clinic which provides a *problem finding* environment but not a *problem preventing* environment.'

The MDC was open five days a week, and a focus for clinical expertise throughout the area. Tomlinson argued that it could prevent problems like the 'diabetic foot' – the commonest cause of in-patient admission and (if amputation was required) the most likely reason for a lengthy stay. Better integrated health care might cost less overall. Furthermore, such initiatives could add to the research profile of the UMH as was shown by the High Risk Diabetic Foot Clinic set up by Andrew Boulton in the late 1980s, in conjunction with the Northern College of Chiropody, which went on to develop a world-class reputation as a centre of excellence for practice and research on the 'foot at risk'.

Nursing expertise was crucial to these services, and with the help of Jill Pooley, a Diabetes Specialist Nurse, Tomlinson established a series of mini-clinics in the surgeries of general practitioners. These clinics were also intended to educate and reassure general practitioners that the treatment and monitoring of diabetic patients did not have to be a hospital activity, whilst also addressing concerns that the Centre was just another *hospital* innovation diverting funds away from primary care.

In the 1990s another readily accessible, non-hospital based centre, the Manchester Sickle Cell and Thalassaemia Centre opened, incorporating services originally run by a health centre in the Moss Side district. In this instance, Manchester's ethnic communities, aided by the CHC and other health activists, persuaded administrators not to place the Centre in the grounds of the hospital, in order to maintain its close ties to the community.

The Nursing Process, *Project 2000*, and nurse-practitioners

The nursing profession changed substantially during the late 1970s and 1980s, partly through the growing influence of academic nursing on the theory and practice of nursing in general. The University's own School of Nursing expanded throughout the 1970s in terms of staff, undergraduates and advanced degree programmes, but it

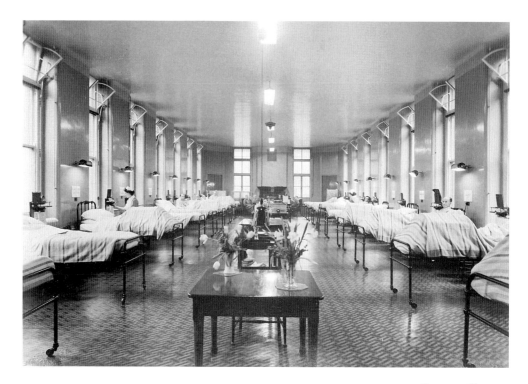

was through the introduction of the 'Nursing Process' that the School began to significantly affect the life and work of the MRI. The Nursing Process supplanted the traditional 'task assignment' model of nursing, whereby a nurse would be given a specific task – such as disposing of bed-pans – to be performed for every patient. The new approach was oriented to individual patients; it stressed systematic note-taking of a patient's 'nursing history', on a data sheet designed to identify an individual's nursing needs and to guide the subsequent nursing method. The analysis of results and outcomes, as a critical part of this process, was also enabled by the new data sheets introduced by the School.

The Nursing Process established practical nursing on a theoretical basis quite different from the medical management model with which it coexisted. Thus the responses to the Process reflected the different attitudes to the autonomy of nursing and the relationships of doctors and nurses. A key instigator in the introduction of the Process to Manchester and the MRI, Nurse-Researcher Frances Roberts, described some of the early reactions amongst nurses themselves: 'Essentially, it was a very, very sensible idea. Instead of the Ward Sister writing out a list of tasks for all the nurses to do, based on what she … knew about the condition of all the patients, every patient would be looked at as an individual … [There was a] lot more resistance in the early stages, because it meant a lot more writing than nurses had ever done. Prior to the Nursing Process the … night report to the Day Staff consisted of a large book … with comments like … 'slept well'. So it didn't really tell you everything about the patient! You had to go to a number of different sheets to find out … It was fine if your ward wasn't too busy and you had plenty of nurses, but if you got short of staff it became very time-consuming!'

For Roberts and others in the School of Nursing, the data produced through the Nursing Process became valuable raw material

Figure 21. By the 1980s and 1990s, attempts were made to create more private space around each bed.

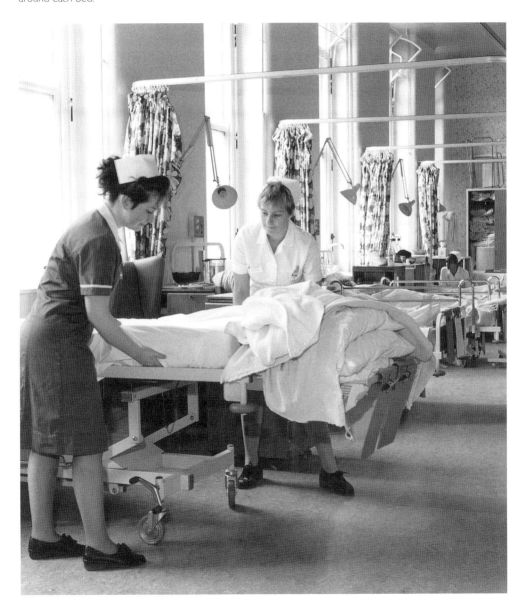

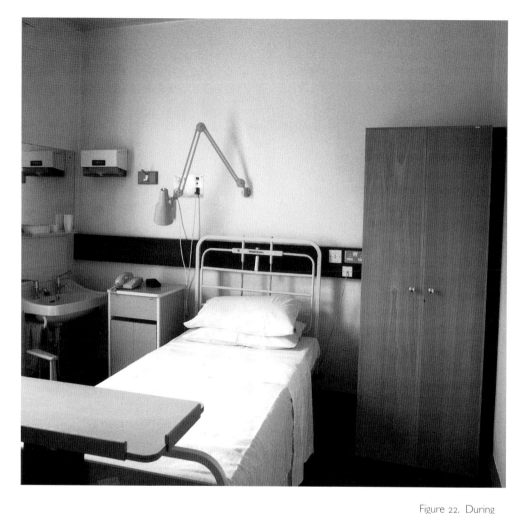

Figure 22. During the 1980s the Infirmary created more single occupancy rooms.

to be fed into the developments in Information Processing then underway in the MRI, particularly through the office of the Director of Finance. During the 1980s, the MRI's Nursing Process made Manchester a prominent model of good practice, which many tried to replicate elsewhere.

Another academic-inspired model of nursing also emerged during the 1980s, building on themes underpinning the Nursing Process, but also raising issues of perennial concern. *Project 2000*, published by the United Kingdom Central Council in 1986, tried to end the reliance of hospitals upon the labour of student nurses, and to rebalance the education of nurses away from ward work, towards college education. All schools of nursing were to link themselves to institutions of higher education, and extra staff would be introduced for routine work on the wards, so allowing nursing students more time to observe and learn.

Project 2000 also reflected themes emerging simultaneously in medical education – for example, the desirability of incorporating more primary care and community medicine into professional curricula. But *Project 2000* deliberately distanced nursing from medicine, presenting medical education as disease-focused whilst nursing was to be *health*-focused. This characterization antagonized some doctors, as did practical problems associated with the new bureaucratic structures and ward routines. But the changes were also controversial amongst nurses. As Christine Hallett reported in her study of the impact of *Project 2000*: 'educational programmes were radically restructured to accommodate a greater primary health care element and to give emphasis to the study of health and normality. Ward staff and community nurses alike found themselves working with students who had a different background of knowledge and experience than those they had supervised previously. At the same time, confusion surrounded the new status of nursing students, which led to a tendency for nurses to resent and distrust the fact that these students were "supernumerary".' Despite these and other problems, *Project 2000* was taken up across the nation's hospitals during the early 1990s.

While assistants were being introduced to remove routine tasks from nurses, some nurses were being trained for tasks previously restricted to doctors. The late 1970s and 1980s saw the appearance of the 'nurse-practitioner', for example the Diabetes Specialist Nurse. When Stephen Tomlinson sought to change the disorganized, 'doctor-dominated' culture of diabetes services in Manchester and the North West by establishing a new centre, he chose Jill Pooley, a Diabetes Specialist Nurse, to help him to do this. The partnership enabled Pooley to escape the restrictive 'delegated task' role then typical of diabetic nursing; and by Tomlinson's own enthusiastic admission, she also changed the way he practised medicine, shifting him away from a narrow academic focus towards a more holistic, patient-centred and education-intensive approach.

Just as the coronary care and renal units had allowed nurses to specialize and develop expertise in the late 1960s and 1970s, so in the 1980s facilities like the Manchester Diabetes Centre presented new opportunities to nurses wishing both to specialize and to gain some say in the *direction* of research and practice. The importance of this connection between specialist nursing and the University's School of Nursing may be seen in Pooley's efforts to pioneer distance-learning packages for diabetes nurses, as well as developing a nursing diploma course in diabetes – both of which were to become highly popular and well-regarded, nationally and internationally.

The 1980s: bed-cuts, budget-cuts and more restructuring

Between the 1940s and 1980s, Manchester had changed a great
deal. Slum clearance and new residential building projects meant
that large numbers of citizens left the inner city to start new lives
in the expanding suburbs This had an inevitable impact on the
planning and provision of hospital services. Though the MRI, Royal
Eye and St. Mary's hospitals had large numbers of beds in part to
serve as teaching facilities for the University's Medical School, the
reduction of the local population meant these Central District bed
numbers were increasingly eyed as a potential source of financial cuts,
especially when teaching facilities were becoming well established
in South Manchester and Salford. In 1981, a Joint DHSS and
North West Regional Health Authority working party announced
its plans to close 700 beds across Manchester and Salford in order
to redistribute resources out of the old urban core and into the
surrounding districts.

The announcement was of immediate concern to the MRI:
although new regional specialty beds were to be established in
the Central District, overall the hospitals would lose 250 beds.
Documents suggesting that the planned bed-cuts might be drastically
brought forward were leaked to the *Manchester Evening News*, and
provoked a storm of protest. Central District consultants set up an
Action Committee to oppose the proposals, supported by the District
Authority and the Community Health Council, who organized a
public campaign of opposition, collecting 28,000 signatures in only
six weeks. Consultants and public campaigners were soon joined by
the Joint Consultative Committee (a joint staff and management
committee set up to promote good relations), and by the Joint Shop
Stewards Committee representing staff interests. Lobbying of local
MPs secured their support and Manchester City Council passed a
resolution against the proposals. The Regional Authority responded
to the campaign by setting up a number of consultative bodies and a
review of the plans. As a result, the number of beds to be cut in the
Central District was reduced to 176, and the Doctor's Action Group
was invited to produce its own long-term plan.

The financial stringency around the time of the 1982 NHS reforms
also extended to the university sector. In 1981 the government
announced that Manchester University would face cuts of 16% over
three years, a move that threatened future planning and development
of University facilities. The Medical Faculty faced an overall reduction
of 13.3%, with a 12.5% reduction in areas with clinical commitments
to patient care, and a 15.8% reduction in other areas. The cuts led
inevitably to a reduction in posts and hiring-freezes throughout the

Figure 23. This aerial photograph of the Infirmary taken in the early 1980s shows the massive clearance of slum housing from around the hospital, opening up areas for car-parks and large-scale building projects. The St. Mary's tower block (opened in 1970) can be seen front centre, with the MRI at centre, and the Royal Eye Hospital towards the top left of the picture.

Faculty. Despite warnings from the University Grants Committee, that same year the University had increased its undergraduate medical student intake to 300 more than the recommended number, both risking a fine and placing great pressure on the resources of the medical school and hospitals.

But an unexpected silver lining glimmered. As the Dean of the Medical School, J.M. Evanson, wrote in a 1981 letter to *Mediscope*: 'Reduction in formal, didactic teaching may be necessary, but this is a process which has long been urged by many of us in the Faculty and it is not out of keeping with the concept of the University as a place of learning rather than a "school".' Evanson also pointed out that the traditionally strong relationship between Faculty and NHS staff promised to ease the pressure, with hospital staff across the region taking a greater interest in undergraduate and postgraduate teaching. Such regional teaching was indeed evident, and not just in hospitals. In 1986, for example, a new fourth year 8–week module was introduced to the clinical curriculum: for their 'General and Community Practice' module, students were based in one or two regional health districts, moving between geriatrics, community medicine, occupational medicine, community paediatrics and general practice. These new methods of organization were expected to bring enduring benefits, even within the financially depressed NHS of the 1980s.

CHAPTER FIVE

The MRI within the Central Trust, 1990–2002

DURING THE 1980s, the Thatcher government had considered a shift to an insurance-based system of health care, following Continental models, but had been deterred by the prospect of massive public protest against any undermining of the NHS as a public service. The Minister of Health, Kenneth Clark, was happy to retain funding from tax, but he wanted to reduce professional control and to introduce 'market principles' to the NHS, using a model from an American health economist who suggested that GPs could be used as 'purchasers' of hospital services. Such principles underpinned Clark's 1989 White Paper, *Working for Patients*, upon which the 1990 NHS and Community Care Act was based. The Act forced a separation of purchasing and provision, in an attempt to increase competition and improve efficiency within the NHS, but also as a means to devolve power and responsibility to the local level.

This move away from centralization was very significant. Since 1948, money had passed from the Ministry to Regions and then to Hospital Districts, and the sums involved had been calculated largely on the basis of historic costs. From the early 1970s, allocations had increasingly depended on the populations served and their special needs. But as of 1 April 1991, all NHS hospitals began to operate within a system whereby they received some of their money on the basis of the number of patients treated. NHS money would now 'follow the patient'. General Practices were encouraged to become 'fund holders', receiving amounts of NHS money that corresponded to their patient lists, with the freedom to spend it on services at hospitals of their choice. Alternatively, they could develop their own GP services to substitute for hospital treatments, for example minor surgery. Major hospitals were encouraged to become independent Trusts, attracting patients and funds from both District Health Authorities and from GP fund-holders.

The planners of these reforms anticipated that as hospitals competed for patients, superior services would develop and expand, while the poorer ones would fail and close. Such was the logic, though the constraints of geography, the need for secure funding of emergency services, and the limited number of practices and hospitals that chose to 'go independent', substantially restricted the operation of this 'internal market'.

By bidding to become self-governing Trusts, hospitals were able to set budgets, plan services, borrow money and draw up contracts and performance criteria for staff. We shall see in this chapter how the new system dealt with the long recognized need for a substantial rebuilding of the central hospitals. We shall defer to the next and last chapter an analysis of other, wider issues that interacted with the ongoing plans for the central hospitals. In the present chapter, we retain our focus on the MRI and its immediate neighbours, starting from 1990, as they considered their future under a new set of Conservative NHS reforms. For the Central Manchester teaching hospitals, here was a chance to regain something of the independence they had enjoyed before their 1974 integration into the regional structure. As a Trust they could hope to deal more easily and profitably with a range of health districts, not just the one in which they were situated. Across the country, some consultants and many managers welcomed the prospect, but other consultants and staff worried about the increased clerical and managerial costs, and feared the development of a two-tier system with 'sink' hospitals in poorer districts. Arguments were fierce and the government allowed ballots to decide – but they ensured that the financial rewards spoke strongly in favour of 'self-government', and managers were left in no doubt as to where their futures lay.

Thus in 1991, the MRI, St. Mary's, the Royal Eye Hospital and the Dental Hospital became the Manchester Central Hospitals and Community Care National Health Service Trust, one of the 57 new trusts established across England and Wales that year. Two years later the Trust was renamed the Central Manchester Healthcare (NHS) Trust, when community services were devolved to form their own organi-zation. At this point the Northern College of Chiropody ceased to be the fifth point of the old 'UMH star' to become part of the Mancunian Community NHS Trust; it is now part of the Central Manchester Primary Care NHS Trust, operating as part of the Rusholme Health Centre. The historic dual role of the foot hospital in supporting the acute sector through the provision of specialist services, and in providing community-sector services, continues to this day.

For the other four hospitals, the decision to become a Trust was taken in the face of much local opposition, as shown by a poll commissioned by the British Medical Association (BMA) in which consultants in Manchester and Salford voted 81% against the move. Opposition notwithstanding, reform and restructuring continued apace. The Council Chair of the BMA complained

Figure 24. The Central Manchester Healthcare Trust was named in 1993 following the division of the Manchester Central Hospitals and Community Care Trust (formed in 1991) into separate entities. In 2001 the Central Manchester Healthcare Trust joined with the Manchester Children's Hospitals Trust to become the Central Manchester and Manchester Children's University Hospitals Trust.

in 1992 that: 'The strategy seems to be to press ahead with all speed on the principal that it is better to swallow unpleasant medicine in one gulp than prolong the agony ... We think otherwise: there are major side-effects and it would be better not to take the potentially fatal dose and then have to reach for the stomach-pump.' But new trusts continued to spring up across the country as hospital managers jumped at the chance to have more say in their own planning and more opportunities to borrow and build.

As commentators like Steve Harrison of Manchester University have pointed out, here was a new kind of reform. There was now no detailed national plan, as there had been in 1948, 1974 and 1983; instead possibilities were opened and incentives created so that parts of the system could move to new arrangements whilst others remained, more or less, with the old. Here indeed was a new flexibility; but as the next 20 years were to show, successive piecemeal reforms, separately introduced for different aspects of a complex system, could produce a bewildering array of shifting structures with different agendas and geographical boundaries. Co-ordination, 'joint-working' and 'continuity of care' remained as ideals, but they were not easily achieved when formal arrangements, job designations and job holders changed every two or three years.

Administrative restructuring under the new Central Trust

For the architects and supporters of the new Central Trust, devolution of management responsibility to clinical providers was a priority, leading to a system of 'clinical directorates' within which nurses, doctors, other health professionals and managers worked alongside each other. In Manchester, a Directorate of Clinical and

Non-Clinical Support Services provided facilities for all other directorates, as did the various departments of the corporate headquarters. The clinical directors together with the corporate directors comprised the Trust Management Executive, the new governing body for the central hospitals. This Management Executive took overall responsibility for developing Trust policy, monitoring performance and major strategic decisions. It was guided by five Sub-Committees – Human Resources, Finance, Estates and Assets, Strategic Planning, and Clinical Issues – each chaired by a non-executive director. A Director of Finance (and later a Director of Human Resources) provided strategic advice and planning, and a Nursing (and later also a Medical) Director oversaw staffing and quality assurance issues. The Chief Executive of the Trust was accountable for the management and delivery of services across the hospitals, and for reporting on these to the Board. This arrangement consolidated the move away from team management towards business-like structures, which followed the Griffiths Report of 1984.

The Board itself was led by a Chairman with overall responsibility for the management of the Trust. Several non-executive directors were appointed from the local civic or medical communities, each bringing expertise in some specific area, such as serving particular patient groups or providing services in the community. The Trust Board were keen to be as transparent as possible, and in 1995 began to hold their bi-monthly formal meetings in public, some four years before the government implemented legislation making this compulsory. In a further effort to increase transparency and community participation, the Central Manchester Community Health Council were invited to attend all Board meetings.

Throughout this time the management of the Central hospitals continued to attract considerable criticism, but nonetheless, the new Trust was widely commended through the various schemes then being used to encourage good management practices across the public and private sectors. In 1996, it was one of only fourteen trusts to be awarded the Charter Mark – for organizations providing excellent service to the public – for *all* its activities. Similarly, in 1998 the Trust became the largest health care organization in the UK to win one of the government's Investors in People Awards – for excellence in employee communication and training.

The Medical Directorate

Initially, there were six clinical directorates within the Central Trust – Medical, Surgical, St. Mary's, Dental Hospital, Royal Eye

Hospital, and Psychiatry. By the end of the decade, these categories had been reorganized and expanded, and the Trust went in to the new millennium with Directorates for Acute Surgery, Clinical Radiology, Dental Services, Specialist Surgical Services, Laboratory Medicine, the Manchester Heart Centre, Medicine, MRI Theatres (with Anaesthesia and Sterile Services), Ophthalmology, Psychiatry, Rehabilitation, St. Mary's, Facilities, and Research and Development. By the end of the 1990s, the Trust had greatly extended its involvement in community medicine. In addition to the Manchester Diabetes Centre, it established a number of high profile outreach services, including community psychiatric nursing based in the Kath Locke Community Resource Centre, and new services in the St. Mary's Sexual Assault Centre. In addition, a Maternity Pilot Project targeted patients for whom English was not a first language, and patients experiencing problems with mental health or drugs; a Trust midwife worked with an independent midwife and with voluntary link workers based in the community.

The Medical Directorate was from the outset the Trust's largest, incorporating a wide range of specialties in 'Natural Clinical Groups' (NCGs), each steered by a clinical manager and a directorate nurse, with responsibility for day-to-day management of the group. The NCGs were: cardiology (which transferred to the Surgical Directorate when it amalgamated with cardiothoracic surgery to become the Heart Unit in 1993), clinical haematology, endocrinology and diabetes, general medicine, genito-urinary medicine, neurosciences, nuclear medicine, renal medicine, and the Robert Barnes Medical Unit. The split between general medicine and specialty admissions was approximately 60:40, with ischaemic heart disease, renal failure, myocardial infarction, cerebrovascular accident, chronic obstructive airways disease and diabetes mellitus making up half of all specialty admissions.

The Heart Unit was a major provider of tertiary care for regional referrals. It gained national press attention in 1993 for implanting the country's first pectoral defibrillator, and again when, at a cost of £100,000, it installed a state-of-the-art electro-physiological laboratory system for diagnosing rare heart palpitations. The Regional Renal Transplant Centre was also a major focus for referrals, and attracted much international attention throughout the decade. In 1993 (the thirtieth anniversary of the Manchester Renal Unit), it secured additional funding from the Regional Health Authority to continue to build up its renal transplant list, at that time one of the busiest in Europe, and it embarked on a successful, if limited, venture into pancreatic transplantation. The Centre's successes were often reported in the national press, and its public profile was raised further through the work of Mr Neil Parrott, an MRI consultant surgeon, in the organization of the World Transplant Games held in Manchester in 1995.

The mid 1990s saw a staffing crisis for the Medical Directorate as new rules on the working hours of junior doctors came into force. During the 1980s, several groups of junior doctors had run well-publicized campaigns against individual hospitals and authorities, protesting the number of hours they were forced to work. Public outrage and concern over the 100+ hour week led to government intervention and the imposition of targets on Regional Authorities. By 1994 the North West Region had achieved its targets, ensuring that the overwhelming majority of junior doctors worked no more than 72 hours per week. In Manchester, these results were achieved through the efforts of a task force chaired by Dr Stephen Horsley and involving the Postgraduate Dean, Professor Ian Houston, together with nursing, technical and junior hospital staff. Thus Clinical Groups had to adapt to a reduction of some 25% in the hours that house officers were permitted to spend on the wards. They coped by creating ward-based teams supporting a central medical assessment unit for new admissions: following initial assessments, patients were sent to one of four specially designated wards which together provided about 100 beds. At a time when the MRI, along with the nation's other hospitals, struggled against a shortage of doctors, such organizational innovations facilitated emergency medical admissions, and also ensured that overstretched staff did not have to travel all over the hospital to check on new arrivals.

The Surgical Directorate

The original Surgical Directorate covered 10 Natural Clinical Groups: Accident and Emergency, Trauma and Orthopaedics, General Surgery, Urology, Renal Transplants, Vascular Surgery, Cardiothoracic, ENT, Critical Care, and Theatres. The reputation of all units and departments across the Directorate grew steadily during the 1990s. The Surgical Directorate's Cochlear Implant Service, for instance, was the only one of its kind in the North West, attracting adults and children from across the country. In 1993 the Directorate opened a new parent-support centre, and achieved a national first when ENT surgeon Mr Richard Ramsden carried out a successful brain-stem implant.

On the teaching and research side too, MRI-based services received attention and praise. The growing expertise in laparoscopic techniques, for example, attracted many surgeons to the City, eager to learn new techniques and so reduce the time that patients needed

Figure 25. The Wolfson Centre for Minimally Invasive Surgery opened on the MRI site in 1995, then one of four such education and training facilities in the UK.

to spend in hospital. These training efforts were much advanced through the opening of the Wolfson Centre for Minimally Invasive Therapy at the MRI in October 1995, one of four such facilities in the UK set up to train surgeons and minimize the errors and complications associated with the increasingly popular 'key-hole' techniques. In Manchester's case, the £300,000 grant secured by Professor Rory McCloy enabled the Trust to offer courses in laparoscopy, pleuroscopy and basic surgical skills, particularly in general surgery and gynaecology. The Centre's new simulator enabled surgeons to explain the theoretical underpinnings of the techniques through demonstration, and also provided invaluable opportunities for Senior House Officers and other trainees to safely gain hands-on experience. Other initiatives in advanced training included tele-links between ten operating theatres and the Postgraduate and Health Sciences Centre, to which operations were transmitted live, so facilitating a range of courses for students, staff and outside organizations. Alongside these successes came some considerable hardship, however, as the Surgical Directorate experienced lean years during the mid 1990s, mainly due to contract shortfalls.

The development of other Central Trust Directorates in the 1990s

Dental

For many decades the state of the teeth of Manchester had been a cause of serious concern. The 1990s saw a vigorous fund-raising effort directed at local and national groups for the creation of a new Dental Education Centre. The School's reputation for education was already impressive: by the mid 1990s some 25% of all postgraduate dental students in England and Wales had passed through its doors. When the new Educational Centre opened in 1998, £2.25 million had been collected, and the fund continued to expand. All branches of the profession were served by the Centre including dental therapists, hygienists, technicians and nurses. Also in 1998, the Dental Hospital was nominated as the regional centre for the management of specialized Cleft Lip and Palate services. This service brought together a range of specialists, including surgeons, orthodontists and speech and language therapists, and became a template for 15 new regional centres across the UK. That same year saw the establishment in Manchester of the Cochrane Centre for Oral Health, one of a range of international centres covering many areas of medicine, which collected and analysed research results as a basis for 'evidence-based practice.'

Psychiatry

The early 1990s were very significant for the Psychiatry Directorate. The new Winnicott Centre – a £600,000, purpose-built facility close to the Oxford Road site – brought child and adolescent psychiatry alongside child psychology, and acted as the headquarters of the Regional service. Soon afterwards the Edale Unit was opened, offering acute inpatient and respite facilities for old age psychiatry, so completing a full 'mental health campus' on the site, including the Rawnsley Day Hospital and the York House old age psychiatry centre. At Gaskell House, the home of the psychotherapy services, facilities were upgraded through extensive refurbishment of buildings. And throughout the 1990s, the Directorate underscored the Trust's commitment to community medicine by providing teams of nurses and other professionals for a number of projects across the City and Region, designed to reach and treat patients who were not normally 'compliant'.

Laboratory services

The other major building project during the early 1990s involved a radical overhaul of laboratory services within the Trust and the

Region. The Trust's Laboratory Directorate aimed to improve access and efficiency by breaking down traditional professional boundaries, so providing a single unified service. By the end of the decade, the Directorate would provide round the clock services to Trust staff, local GPs and other users. A £15 million state-of-the-art building – Clinical Sciences –– was opened in 1994, bringing together microbiology, biochemistry, histopathology, and the City Mortuary. It thus realized an ambition which had been vigorously pursued since the 1970s, but demonstrable from the early years of the NHS – to rationalize laboratory resources.

The Eye Hospital
Increasing numbers of patients in the 1980s and 1990s placed Manchester Royal Eye Hospital under considerable strain, although the appointment of more nurse-practitioners and consultants, together with the expansion of day-case facilities and accommodation, went some way to easing the burden. Whilst retaining its secondary and emergency referral services for the local population, the hospital worked to strengthen its specialist training and medical services, including the Emergency Eye Centre, the Acute Referral Centre, Ophthalmic Imaging, the Ultrasound Unit, Electrodiagnosis, the Laser Unit, Optometry, Orthoptics, the Manchester Eye Bank and the Ocular Prosthetics Department. The Eye Hospital had by then become the second largest postgraduate teaching centre in the UK (London's Moorfields being the largest).

St. Mary's
By the 1990s, St. Mary's had again expanded its activities to include the introduction of new techniques of minimally invasive surgery, a nurse-led cervical-smear screening clinic, a new outpatients clinic devoted to the detection of inherited cancers, and (in conjunction with the Department of Genetics and the Genetic Counselling Service) a new cytogenetic database system. In 1995, services that had been transferred out of St. Mary's decades earlier returned to the hospital when the day-case obstetric unit for women with complications of pregnancy closed in Withington and reopened on Hathersage Road. The facilities for child patients at the hospital also increased, including the opening in 1996 of a new children's outpatients department. The ongoing sub-specialization of the hospital further advanced the role of St. Mary's as a regional referral centre for women and children, bringing into sharp relief the continual need to carefully balance the growth of tertiary services with the supply of largely secondary services to local residents. The tertiary development of the hospital continues apace, and not just in regional

terms: in 2001 the Department of Genetics was successful in its bid to become one of the two National Reference Laboratories for Genetics, bringing in many millions of pounds in extra funding.

Completion of Phases I and II: a new look for the Oxford Road site

The Trust site's multi-million pound rebuilding programme reached partial completion when the new Phase I and Phase II clinical buildings were formally opened by HRH Diana, the Princess of Wales in July 1992, to considerable local celebration and media attention. The

Figure 26. The official opening of the Phase I and II Infirmary redevelopment was celebrated with a visit from Princess Diana.

Phase I restructuring programme included the £3.1 million refurbishment of the former Out-Patients' Department of the MRI so as to re-house the Infirmary's Physiotherapy Department; the redevelopment of the old X-ray Department into a £2.6 million Postgraduate Health Sciences Centre; the completion of the new Edale Unit providing mental health facilities; and the beginning of work on the new laboratory and X-ray buildings. The Phase II development of the Manchester Royal Infirmary comprised a new main surgical complex, an Accident and Emergency Department, outpatient suites and a number of other services. Several of the Infirmary's mid twentieth century buildings were demolished; what remained was largely a mix of the Edwardian and the very new.

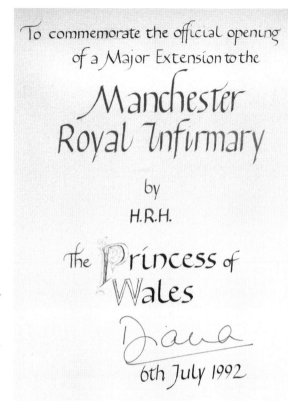

To commemorate the official opening of a Major Extension to the

Manchester Royal Infirmary

by

H.R.H.

The Princess of Wales

Diana

6th July 1992

Figure 27.

The successful completion of Phase I and Phase II was heartening, but in 1991 and 1992 the Central Trust was seriously overspent. The short-fall prompted bed closures, cut-backs to surgical lists, a freeze on recruitment to the Phase II facilities, an appearance on *Panorama* by Dr David Warrell, the Trust's Chief Executive, and vehement criticism from the local branch of the British Medical Association (which had opposed the internal market reforms). Ironically, the cash shortfall came at a time of rising productivity for the Infirmary, as 5% more patients were treated with only a 1% rise in additional costs. But the national deal for new trusts had involved calculations made at 1989 running costs, and, as trusts were not allowed to set their own cost per patient until 1994, it soon became clear that there would be no immediate prospect of the Central Trust generating more income, either by borrowing extra money or by establishing new and more lucrative contracts.

For critics, the early months of the Central Trust appeared to confirm their fears. The promised 'flexibility' had resulted in the Central Trust recouping costs through cutting surgical lists and staff recruitment; or, as detractors put it: 'the freedom to cut costs rather than improve services'. The system's supporters, however, saw it all very differently. They argued that when the trust system matured, the Central Trust would be well placed to compete, not only with nearby hospitals: 'but also as a tertiary specialist centre offering highly sophisticated services to draw in patients from well beyond the local area' – so stated the General Manager of the MRI, Mr Hathaway, in the pages of the students magazine, *Mediscope*, in 1991.

That the MRI and other Central Trust hospitals should become such a draw was of the utmost importance. In 1991 some 98.5% of the Trust's money had come from block service-grants, not as money per patient. As the market was due to be more fragmented and competitive, all hospitals risked a fall in income, certainly in guaranteed income, and for hospitals such as the MRI which traditionally drew patients from outside its own area, it was crucial that its specialized services out-stripped those of patients' local hospitals. One striking market success was the open-heart surgery contract won for patients from South Wales in 1992; but overall the issue was an ongoing headache for the Trust.

Specialization and the Central Trust

The ever-sharper focus on specialization and academic medicine within the Trust had its critics. There seemed few guarantees that a comprehensive local medical and surgical service could, or would, be maintained through the contract system. For students too, specialization posed problems. Soon after the introduction of the Trust, the Dean of Manchester Medical School, Professor Robert Boyd, wrote in *Mediscope* that the teaching of general medicine and surgery would suffer if the hospitals continued to become more specialized: 'Already there are third year medical students emerging from an eight week surgical attachment having seen the repair of several aortic aneurysms but not hernia repairs or varicose vein operations'. Others disagreed, arguing that students should not be forced to learn from common conditions. Boyd's colleague and Postgraduate Dean, the psychiatry professor Neil Kessel, argued that students should not simply learn to treat symptoms, but ought rather to: 'understand the pathological processes underpinning those symptoms'. Thus, students *needed* to see patients who demonstrated important medical principles – the 'interesting cases' referred to a teaching hospital for specialist treatment or investigation.

Whatever their position on specialization and medical education, most academics could agree with the findings of a report by the NHS charity, The King's Fund, which suggested that changing regimes of patient management threatened established patterns of medical instruction. Ever-shorter hospital stays for patients and reduced bed-capacity, meant an uncertain future for traditional bedside teaching. More and more patients were being treated in the community, partly because new treatments were increasingly managed by general practitioners. How then were clinical students to learn? Although students could be sent out to GP practices to gain some experiences, Manchester's Clinical Dean, Mike Cheshire, was keen to stress the limits of such an exercise: 'You have to understand what can be taught in the community and what cannot. GPs can teach communication skills, history taking and examination, but they are less likely to have in depth specialist skills such as neurology. Students will also miss the management of acutely ill patients.' Similarly, teaching through outpatient clinics presented numerous problems – although ideally it would be a chance for students to see 'living pathology', in reality suitable teaching cases were thin on the ground.

Such problems were raised at a time of great change to medical education in Manchester and elsewhere. Calls for reform at the national level from the General Medical Council (GMC) combined with local concerns to produce major reform of the clinical curriculum and a complete restructuring of the pre-clinical programme.

Education and curriculum reform

In 1991 the Manchester Medical School began a wide-ranging investigation into medical education in Manchester and elsewhere. They intended a fundamental reform of their own curriculum, especially the pre-clinical course. Of particular interest was the 'problem-based approach' – then under review by the British GMC as part of their *Tomorrow's Doctors* investigations. It was apparently working well at other medical schools, notably Maastricht in Holland, Newcastle in Australia, McMaster in Canada and Harvard in the USA. For each week of such courses, a clinical case would be presented to students, who then had to research the basic science needed to understand the diagnosis and subsequent treatment. Advocates of the method claimed that it encouraged students to become autonomous learners; their individual responsibility and personal interests were further extended through a range of options, and by examinations that stressed understanding rather than regurgitation of facts. The problem-based approach was also seen as bridging the gap between pre-clinical and clinical segments of the course, by always highlighting the relevance of basic science to clinical practice.

With reports from working parties generally favourable to the introduction of the problem-based approach, the Medical School created a new post of Senior Lecturer to oversee the design and conversion to a new curriculum. But some staff were sceptical. As one now retired Trust consultant put it: 'It is alright for some forms of instruction, but not for everything. The problem solving with actors or people mimicking is just not the same as being in the smelly room with the dirty curtains and the person writhing with some severe problems and so on.' The new system was introduced to the School in 1995, accompanied by a Clinical Skills Laboratory opened at Withington, offering a variety of Computer Assisted Learning packages to underpin the clinical situations presented to students.

For the students themselves, the drastic reduction in lectures, the overhaul of the examination system and the introduction of small group tutorials were all trumpeted through the pages of *Mediscope* as greatly improving the educational experience. The new approach depended heavily on the motivation of the individual student, for good or for bad; as an ex-Dean of the School put it: 'If you have a mind and want to use it … PBL is a way of doing that, and I think its a potent way. But it certainly means that there's a longer period of insecurity, because if you don't have a structured course people are never quite sure what they've done and what they've not done. And certainly the more vulnerable students found that. But it *is* clearly producing doctors with a thinking approach to medicine, and that's what it is intended to do.' In 1995 the School was visited by the Health Minister, Steven Dorrell, to celebrate the scheme, and to highlight the potential benefits of sweeping curriculum change to other, as yet undecided medical schools.

New research and new Directorates

The Radiology Directorate established in the mid 1990s pioneered efforts to bring together NHS staff, industry, and the academics. The collaboration made possible a £15 million, 5-year investment in radiological services in the Trust, and led to extensive new research facilities. In 1998, a new European centre of excellence in brain scanning – the Ian Isherwood Magnetic Resonance Imaging Centre was opened. Industrial support was vital, and Philips Medical Systems contributed substantially. The heart of the new facility was a 1.5 Tesla Philips Gyroscan installed in the University Department of Radiology in the Stopford Building, connected through fibre-optic links to a similar scanner in the MRI's Department of Neuroradiology. For the University, too, the new development was important: the state-of-the-art scanning facilities provided a great boost to the multi-disciplinary Institute of Neurosciences, a growing research presence within the University. For their part, Philips designated the joint MRI-University Centre as their European Research and Development site for magnetic resonance imaging in the neurosciences.

In 1997, another collaborative bid (from the Central Trust, the University of Manchester, the South Manchester University Hospitals Trust, and the Salford Royal Hospitals Trust) succeeded: a Wellcome-funded Clinical Research Centre brought an extra £3.5 million to the city and was built near the MRI. The facility was designed for patient-orientated clinical research, through the provision of research beds for inpatients, areas for research outpatient clinics and associated research laboratory and investigation spaces. That Manchester had succeeded in a Wellcome competition with 36 bids and only 5 winners, suggested that the relationship between clinical and basic science in Manchester was well regarded by national and international clinical researchers. As the new Chief Executive, James Barbour noted in his Annual Report for the year 1997/8: 'For this Trust, the Wellcome Centre is an important step in our strategy of developing further our links with the University and it is integral to our re-development plans.'

The Research and Development Directorate spent its early life developing the new Wellcome Trust Clinical Research Facility, and identifying themes and funding strategies for research across the Trust (all supported by new Information Technology initiatives). It also established and managed a Trust Research Grants scheme open to all Trust staff for the funding of 2-year projects. The plan was to invest in research and development so as to bring in additional external funding in the longer term. In the financial year 1996/7, as part of a national exercise to identify and cost research programmes, the Directorate announced that 1064 projects were ongoing, costing £5.1 million to support, with some £9.9 million in external sponsorship. The declaration placed the Central Trust in 15th place overall in a league table of UK research providers, and as the 2nd largest provincial provider (the table also showed the continuing dominance of London centres despite the substantial growth in provincial efforts since the Second World War).

The prioritizing of performance and accountability within the health service served to focus attention on information systems across the Trust. In 1998 the St. Mary's service secured nearly £500,000 from the Government's Modernization Fund to develop an IT-based admission system, linking GPs and the hospital in a pilot scheme trialling for application across the country. By this time, the vast majority of GP surgeries were computerized, and linking their systems to local hospitals was an important advance to closer co-operation in working practices. In 1998, the Directorate for MRI

Theatres, Anaesthesia and Sterile Services was formed against a backdrop of a serious national shortage in theatre staff. As well as improving facilities for existing staff, it was also concerned with the recruitment and training of new staff. Once again, IT formed the basis of resource and staffing reforms across the Directorate operations. Similar desires to increase efficiency through new IT systems were behind the creation of the Facilities Directorate, established around the same time to oversee a wide range of non-clinical services – from security, to records, to catering. Also in 1998, the Trust created a new directorate bringing together the therapists, doctors and nurses involved in rehabilitation. In tandem, the Manchester Health Authority began considering the best location for rehabilitation services for central Manchester – specifically whether the modernized MRI could offer a more suitable home than the Barnes Hospital. In 1998 the Authority announced the results of its findings and in 1999 the facilities moved from Barnes to the Oxford Road site.

Following the successful opening of Clinical Sciences I in 1994, the Director of the Laboratory Services, Keith Hyde, along with several of his colleagues, planned for further rationalization and a new £10 million building – Clinical Sciences II – to concentrate the City's pathology services. With considerable effort, the cytology screening services formerly housed at the Christie Hospital were united with St. Mary's gynaecological oncology services, and the new service at the Trust site quickly grew into one of the largest screening services in Europe. As a second component of the plans, the public health laboratory services, housed at Withington Hospital since the 1960s, also moved to Trust site buildings in 2002. It became part of the new national Health Protection Agency, and one of the UK's largest single pathology services. The final part of the plan was the Automation Laboratory, adding enormous additional capacity to the already substantial output of this Directorate.

The MRI's Private Patients' Home, first opened on the Oxford Road site in 1937, continued to operate within the Trust as the Manchester Clinic Directorate. As a private fee-paying facility, it generated significant revenue for the Trust, and extra resources for patient care. The Clinic building also became home to some of the MRI's upgraded facilities. In 1998, for instance, the thirtieth anniversary of the first kidney transplant in Manchester, the transplantation and tissue-typing services were revamped and relocated to the Manchester Clinic.

The Medical and Surgical Directorates in the late 1990s

In the late 1990s the Surgical Directorate was split in two, with general and vascular surgery, urology, renal transplantation, critical care services and the Manchester Clinic becoming the Acute Surgery Directorate, while the three clinical groups – Trauma and Orthopaedics; Otolaryngology, Maxilo-facial Surgery and Audiology; and the Department of Emergency Medicine – collectively made up the Specialist Surgical Services Directorate. Responding to the priorities set out by their purchasers, Trust managers turned to the development of emergency services, hoping to alleviate the problems and reduce the waiting times. Work began on expanding the MRI's A&E Department, and merging resources with those of the Royal Eye Hospital. The importance of this work, and the role that the MRI's Emergency services provided for the City were underscored in 1996 when the hospital treated the casualties of the IRA bomb-attack in the heart of Manchester's shopping district. The merger of the Emergency Eye Centre with the MRI's A&E Department also provided significant new facilities for MANDOC, the MRI based, out-of-hours GP service which continued to expand in these years. Towards the end of the 1990s, work began to transfer A&E services from Withington to the MRI, again changing the MRI Department and its Medical Assessment Unit. After an additional £1.5 million investment, an Acute Medical Centre was opened in the autumn of 2001.

The opening of the cardiac catheter swing laboratory in the Manchester Heart Unit in 1998 further enhanced Manchester's reputation for state-of-the-art diagnostic and therapeutic services. At the end of the 1990s, the Manchester Heart Centre became a full Directorate. In the staff magazine, *Centre Points*, the Heart Centre's Clinical Manager, Dr Bernard Clarke, noted that: 'Manchester and the North West has one of the worst levels of coronary heart disease in the UK, so we are delighted to have this new state of the art facility for our patients. It will make a major difference to the many people we treat every year.' 1998 also saw celebrations marking the 25th anniversary of Maureen Mooney's kidney transplant, a former MRI patient and the longest British transplant survivor. In 2001, a new Renal Ward with acute renal failure beds was opened on Ward 23, as part of the merger between the MRI and Withington's renal units.

On 19 September 1997, staff and patients in the Directorate received a well-publicized visit from Prince Charles – his first public engagements since the death of the Princess of Wales. The Prince specifically asked to visit clinical haematology and to meet

Figure 28. A major part of the Phase II project was the building of this new Accident and Emergency Department on cleared ground at the back of the old Infirmary buildings.

patients receiving treatment for blood cancers, as part of his support for the Macmillan Cancer Relief charity. In 1999 the Queen visited the Trust as part of a visit to Greater Manchester, and met with several staff and patients. The Princess Royal also visited the Trust, in September 2000 to open the new Bereavement Centre – the first such purpose-built facility in the country, made possible through a donation of £110,000 from the WRVS and a further gift of £5,000 from Macmillan Cancer Relief. As the twentieth century came to an end, such visits drew attention to the status of the Trust's hospitals as regional and national centres.

CHAPTER SIX

Children's Services and the Reorganization of Manchester Hospitals

I N THIS LAST CHAPTER, we step back from the detailed history of the central hospitals to again consider the wider picture – the organization of hospitals in the Manchester conurbation. In the 1990s, several long-standing rationalization issues came to a head, especially around 1996–7. The most important, for the MRI, was the decision to locate a new children's hospital on the central site; but it is useful to consider this decision in the context of the other issues that were running alongside. This chapter will review the questions, the decisions and the after-effects. It will give some of the background on the children's hospitals, and it will end with the merger of the Central Trust and the Children's Trust as they planned for new hospital buildings on the central site.

As we have already seen, a number of Manchester hospital facilities had long been seen as needing replacement – at the central site, clearly, but also at Withington Hospital in South Manchester, and the children's hospitals at Pendlebury and Booth Hall. The need for rebuilding triggered further questions – were the sites appropriate for new hospitals? Did South Manchester need a big hospital at Withington as well as the newer hospital further south at Wythenshawe? Were the Booth Hall and Pendlebury sites appropriate for new children's hospitals? Should they be replaced by a single hospital and where should it be? Did a children's hospital need to be adjacent to a general hospital? And if so, which general hospital site was most suitable?

Similar questions were common to many cities (though remarkably little is written about them). In most British cities, the workhouse hospitals had been developed where land was cheap and the paupers were 'out of the way'; but now, as at Hope Hospital, Salford, such sites might be next to orbital motorways, with easy road access from across the region. In other cases, a hospital built for fresh country air, such as Pendlebury, had long since been surrounded by housing, without much improvement of relative access. Booth Hall seemed tucked away, near a park in a poor district of North Manchester; but districts with few facilities valued what they had – for the employment as well as the services. All of these sites had been occupied by hospitals for a century or so, and in that time, the conurbation had changed, and the hospitals had become much more technical, their various services more interdependent. Accommodating changing hospitals to changing cities was bound to be difficult, not least because of the intense local loyalties that hospitals commanded.

But Manchester had another set of problems, commonly found where a university medical school had more than one teaching hospital. Manchester Medical School had depended solely on the central hospitals, as we have seen, but from the 1960s it also developed teaching and research Hope Hospital in Salford, and at Withington Hospital – whose teaching function was shared with other southern hospitals, including the Christie, and then especially with Wythenshawe hospital as it grew and took over some of Withington's work. By the late 1980s, both these new teaching complexes were nationally recognized for their specialist regional functions – Hope for various branches of surgery and medicine, including neurosurgery and gastroenterology; Withington for psychiatry and geriatrics, and Wythenshawe for cardiovascular and pulmonary work. These research specialisms also involved 'tertiary' services: for example, renal dialysis had developed in South Manchester and at Hope and at the MRI; and neurology was strong both at Hope and the MRI. For some of these special regional services, as we shall see, the purchasing authorities and some service providers came to feel that resources were too thinly spread; in others, the prospect of further specialist development seemed to depend on concentrating the existing services. These questions seemed all the more urgent when the introduction of the internal market complicated and highlighted the financing of tertiary services, and when reductions in the hours to be worked by junior doctors increased the difficulty of staffing intensive services.

These geographical and tertiary-specialism problems were often interactive and additive. They were further complicated by long-standing rivalries between the City Councils of Manchester and Salford, and several of the issues came to a head in the mid 90s, in a period of considerable organizational change. In the early 1990s, all the hospitals concerned had formed new hospital Trusts. In 1993 the Conservative government announced plans to further decentralize and streamline NHS decision-making. Under a 1995 Act, new Health Authorities were formed by combining District Health Authorities with Family Health Service Authorities. The number of health authorities was reduced, and they were constituted as purchasing authorities (so weakening the GP fund-holding arrangements introduced earlier in the decade). They were also granted some powers which were previously regional, and the former Regional Authorities were now reduced to Regional Offices of the (national) Health Service Executive.

So again there was one Health Authority for the whole of Manchester (as in 1974–1982, but now without the three district authorities). For issues that affected more than one authority, the Act stipulated that one of them should act as 'lead', working with the others. The new Health Authority and the Regional Office (under the dynamic leadership of its new head, Donald Wilson) pushed hard for a solution to the City's problems, arousing considerable local opposition.

In such decision processes, the employment of management consultants was now common, and Health Authority managers and their lay Chairs took prominent roles. Some doctors and some members of the public were disturbed by this; they had been raised in a culture where medical decisions were made by doctors, and more general decisions were made by lay councils, of various sorts, advised by doctors and accountants as well as administrators. But the new managers did not see themselves as administrators; their models were more corporate; they could claim delegated political authority from the Secretary of State, and some of them were determined to show that they could resolve long-standing problems. The processes involved public consultations and public meetings, sometimes with several hundred people, and in most cases the decisions were eventually referred to central government. All were then ratified, though sometimes slowly.

The problems shifted, and so did the bodies that were supposed to find solutions. In some cases the debates involved major public campaigns (as over the closure of Withington Hospital in South Manchester); in some cases professionals were divided (as for the location of renal services). Over the question of focusing neurological and neurosurgical developments at Hope or the MRI, professional relations were already strained, and local government rivalries were also involved. The fierce dispute about children's services combined almost all these combustibles.

We will consider the debates in the order just given, culminating in the decision to develop children's services on the central site, and the merger of the Central and Children's Trusts; and for a better understanding of this project, we will include a brief explanation of how the children's hospitals had developed under the NHS. But first we turn to the questions about Central and South Manchester.

The politics of hospital development in the 1990s

South Manchester

A plan to reduce the costs of the South Manchester District Health Authority by consolidating services on one site (so closing either Withington or Wythenshawe hospitals) had been proposed in 1989, and overwhelmingly rejected in a vote of the District Health Authority in February of 1990. But the passing of the 1990 Act restructured this District Health Authority and when a proposal to close one of the hospitals was again tabled in September of that year, the motion was passed easily. Uproar followed as local critics of the national reforms and its effects in Manchester protested that the removal of community representatives from the District Authority had allowed a decision which flew in the face of public opinion.

Led by the local Labour MP, Keith Bradley, the Campaign to Save Withington Hospital attracted much media attention and high profile support from the South Manchester Community Health Council and from hospital staff. But consultants from both Withington and Wythenshawe hospitals voted to support the closure of the Withington Hospital, arguing that redevelopment on a green-field site was vital to the long-term quality of medical services. Academics and administrators from the University of Manchester were also keen for the closure to go ahead, as part of the push towards better facilities for research and teaching.

The Regional and District Authorities bowed to community pressure by postponing plans to close Withington, instead opting for a merger across the two sites, but within months Withington lost its reprieve. The Regional Authority announced that it was to close within 10 years, but with a £20 million investment in Wythenshawe to soften the blow. So began a new phase of wrangling. In 1991, the two hospitals gained Trust status, under a common management, which included the administrators who had advocated unification on one site.

In 1994, the Regional Authority commissioned Professor Duthie to reconsider the problem, and the following year the District Health Authority launched a public consultation over a plan to close Withington, except for day-care and outpatients, and to air plans for the extension of Wythenshawe to include new children's wards. Again, there was huge public opposition, but the District Health Authority persisted, and the Community Health Council, by a very narrow majority, decided not to exert its right to refer the decision to the Secretary of State. The planners assumed that patients who had used Withington would go to Wythenshawe, but it was widely expected that many would in fact go to the central hospitals. We have seen that the Accident and Emergency Service at the MRI was enlarged to cope with the withdrawal of the Withington service.

Renal services

At about the same time, the South Manchester Hospitals were also exercised by debates over the future of renal services. In 1993, the Chronic Renal Failure Advisory Group, set up to co-ordinate services in the Manchester Region, had decided that the services should be concentrated. It was assumed that a service would continue at the MRI, for that was the regional site for renal transplants; but if the Withington service would have to be relocated before long, then perhaps it was time to merge the services of Hope and South Manchester on a site to be decided. In 1995, when Withington's future was darkening, the West Pennine Health Authority led a review of the service on behalf of the health authorities of Greater Manchester. Hope Hospital and South Manchester University Hospital Trust were asked to produce plans for the second site, and these plans were assessed by management consultants. In August 1996 the health authorities presented their choice for public consultation; they preferred to focus the service at Hope, and the MRI. South Manchester Community Health Council objected and the decision was referred to the Secretary of State. But in December 1997, after the election of a Labour Government, the decision for Hope was ratified and the following year saw the establishment of the Greater Manchester Renal Group to oversee reorganization and plan for future service needs. This involved opening several 'easy access' renal clinics, including dialysis services. These 'satellite units' were linked to Hope Hospital in the West sector (covering Trafford, Wigan, Leigh, Bolton, Bury, Rochdale and Oldham), and to the Manchester Royal Infirmary in the East sector (covering Wythenshawe, Stockport, Macclesfield and Tameside).

Neurology and Neurosurgery

The MRI was marginally affected by these developments, but it saw its interests deeply challenged by the debate over neuroscience services. From the mid 1980s, the Regional Authority had wanted to concentrate the development of neurosurgery on a single Greater Manchester site; they were convinced that it was wasteful to have services at North Manchester, Hope and the MRI. That had been the gist of a series of consultations, including a review in 1993 that had recommended Hope for neurosurgery, with Hope and the MRI for neurology. The district health authorities for Manchester and for Salford had jointly put that suggestion to public consultation, but there was strong opposition from Manchester and nothing had been decided, except that Manchester now thought one site should take all the neurosurgery and the majority of the neurology. This preference may have been influenced by the fact that management consultants had judged the MRI more suitable than Hope.

North Manchester was never a likely site for development, but the other two hospitals had strong cases. The MRI had been known for neurosurgery since Jefferson had established an Institute after the Second World War, and the University was keen to develop the service there. Whatever the previous medical school policy about developing specialisms in all three teaching hospitals in accord with the judgements of the medical staff, the Dean of Medicine in the mid 1990s was determined to build up the central site as an international centre for medical sciences; a new tertiary neurosciences block would be a major bridge between university science and clinical medicine. But Hope Hospital too had its traditions and arguments. It was at Salford Royal Infirmary that Jefferson had first developed neurosurgery, and that service had been moved to Hope when the Salford Royal Infirmary was closed. As we have seen, Hope had good access, lots of land, and a national reputation in several branches of medicine, including neurology. Supporters of Hope, including its new Trust chair, Peter Mount, resented the presumptions of the MRI. Importantly, the local patient-groups, who knew the services at the MRI as well as at Hope, much preferred the latter.

The two Trusts were asked to submit proposals and to develop them in collaboration with the (new) Manchester Health Authority; again management consultants were employed to evaluate them. This time, Hope won out, and that was also the preference of the Manchester Health Authority. The proposal was bitterly contested, but agreed by the Manchester Authority in January 1997. It went to the Secretary of State for review, and was confirmed in March. Thereafter there was some concentration of neurological services, but less than the Health Authority had expected. The service at North Manchester relocated to Hope, and some staff transferred from the central site.

Just as had been the case for renal services, the centralization of neurology and neurosurgery was followed by a period of outreach and the provision of satellite units. In this way, for example, Francis Creed, with the support of the University's key planners, developed an academic psychiatry unit in Preston. Not all local doctors were thrilled, but Preston's health service managers were keen to improve facilities and saw the support of Manchester University as a crucial part of that development. The academics, in turn, were able to benefit from excellent clinical links and from the release of NHS financial resources to establish new facilities.

In part, the issue over the location of neuro-services was linked into a wider ongoing discussion about the future of the MRI. How the MRI would be developed was intricately bound to decisions over the future provision of children's services. So here we step back for a deeper historical interlude – to see how the children's hospitals had developed under the NHS.

Children's hospitals, 1948–1990

Paediatrics had been organized as a specialism in Britain since the 1920s, but was limited to a few special hospitals in London and the major provincial centres. Manchester's reputation had been carried by the Ashbys, father and son, who had served as physicians at Pendlebury. From around the Second World War, thanks largely to the salaried posts provided by the NHS, paediatrics grew rapidly and diversified. It was in 1942 that plans were made for the appointment of a Professor of Paediatrics, partly to pull together the paediatricians at the various Manchester and Salford Hospitals. In 1947 Wilfred Gaisford was appointed, and on Catherine Chisholm's retirement from the Duchess of York hospital, he took control there – the first male to hold a senior post. The Manchester Paediatric Club was founded the next year, with Chisholm as a key member; previously she had run a Paediatric Group linking women doctors with child welfare workers. As a woman, she had been excluded from the British Association of Paediatrics.

When the NHS was introduced, it was clear that the pattern of children's hospitals serving Manchester did not fit the district structure of the new organisation. The central hospitals had a small children's Unit that was used for teaching, but the main services were at the Royal Manchester Children's Hospital, Pendlebury (RMCH), Booth Hall Hospital for Sick Children, and at the Duchess of York Hospital. These complemented each other in terms of functions, but were administered by different hospital management committees. Pendlebury came under Salford; Booth Hall and the Duchess were initially grouped with Monsall – the isolation hospital. From 1954, the Duchess, which was in Burnage, was part of the South Manchester group.

During the Second World War and then again in connection with the national *Hospital Plan* of 1962, schemes were devised to concentrate paediatric research into an Institute of Child Health on the central Manchester site, but in fact research remained dispersed, along with the services and teaching. The awkward geography, however, did not prevent paediatricians from playing major roles in the medical school, for example, Robert Boyd (St Mary's), Tim David (Booth Hall) and Ian Houston (RMCH), mostly in the 1980s and '90s.

Pendlebury

The Royal Manchester Children's Hospital in Pendlebury was smaller than Booth Hall in terms of beds, but had a long and prestigious history as a voluntary hospital. Typically, Pendlebury had taken Manchester's surgical cases, and had gained a reputation for orthopaedic surgery under Robert Ollerenshaw. But at the start of the NHS, the physicians were still relying heavily on the healing powers of nature. A convalescent home at St Anne's on Sea had been paid for by Sir William Agnew of the art firm; and from 1934, the Trustees of a London merchant, Zachary Merton, had funded a convalescent home next to the hospital. The average stay in the hospital in the 1930s was about two weeks, but many children stayed much longer. Those with respiratory conditions were nursed in steam-tents and oxygen tents, and steam-sterilization was common on the wards.

By the 1950s, however, it was commonly argued that medicine had changed, and perhaps especially for children. Antibiotics seemed to be conquering infections, and the welfare state seemed to be conquering poverty. The new frontiers in paediatrics would be congenital disorders, metabolic problems and cancer; specialist services would take over the spaces built for convalescence.

Some of Professor Gaisford's interests – BCG vaccinations, care of the newborn, and paediatric oncology – found their place in Pendlebury. Indeed, Gaisford's inauguration of the Manchester Children's Tumour Registry, in association with Edith Paterson at the Christie Hospital, became a model for the world. Under Tim Eden, the RMCH later became a national centre for paediatric oncology including chemotherapy and bone marrow transplants. From the 1950s, specialist fields developed strongly, including paediatric surgery, developmental studies, cardiac work, neurology and orthodontics. George Komrower was a pioneer in the recognition and treatment of inherited metabolic disorders, thus establishing a major centre for genetic medicine; and Aaron Holzel was a leader in cystic fibrosis. The genetic work at Pendlebury achieved a high public profile in the 1990s with Maurice Super's 'Gene Shop' at Manchester Airport. The pathology service, long headed by Basil Marsden, was crucial to these clinical developments (not least to the cancer register).

From around the Second World War, the psychological aspect of child medicine came to the fore, including the effects of hospitalization on children, whatever the diagnosis. Pendlebury developed a strong reputation in child psychiatry; it was also at the forefront of the movement for organized education and play. This movement, now called Action for Sick Children, was a product of the national report, *The Welfare of Sick Children in Hospitals*, written in 1959 by the Manchester orthopaedic surgeon, Sir Harry Platt. Pamela Barnes was another strong local supporter of Action for Sick Children, and the RMCH (for which she recently produced a commemorative volume).

Booth Hall

As we saw in Chapter One, Booth Hall had been a municipal hospital, taking children from 0–16 years of age, for all conditions except acute infectious diseases (which were sent to Monsall). Many of its patients had been long-stay, products of poor urban conditions; and as standards of child heath improved between the wars, inpatient numbers had tended to decline. After the Second World War, as before, the hospital dealt with many polio cases, which were admitted once the infectious phase had passed, and for which it had developed physiotherapeutic facilities. But polio was exceptional; in general, infectious diseases and their aftermaths no longer seemed a major problem. In the extended welfare state, it seemed, almost all children were assured of adequate nutrition; public housing was expanding fast; and hospitals like Booth Hall might fade from use. As we have noted, however, the technological and therapeutic advances of the 1950s and 1960s changed these expectations.

In the 1950s and 1960s, Booth Hall focused on some of the non-infectious dangers – long present, but now more conspicuous. Large numbers of children were burned and scalded by accidents in their own homes, and many had been treated at Wythenshawe where plastic surgery had developed during the Second World War. In 1953, Booth Hall built a new Regional Burns Unit staffed by a general physician, a general surgeon, an orthopaedic surgeon, a plastic surgeon and a large nursing team to deal with the very intensive patient care. Staff from Booth Hall vigorously promoted a series of child safety campaigns, and the regional Poisons Information Centre (founded at Booth Hall in 1962), tried to raise awareness amongst parents of the dangers posed to children through discarded medications in the home.

In 1968, a psychiatric unit was added to Booth Hall, as a direct response to calls from the juvenile courts. It contained 22 beds, consulting rooms, a teaching block and gymnasium. The hospital also developed out-patient psychiatric facilities, and became a regional provider of services. In that same year, a new kidney transplantation and dialysis unit was opened for children whose kidneys had been damaged by fire, accident or disease. The Manchester University renal clinician, Geoffrey Berlyne, oversaw the developments at Booth Hall, and the Booth Hall Unit's director, Mr S. J. Cohen, worked closely with the University and the Infirmary in this uncharted medical territory.

Throughout the 1980s and 1990s, Booth Hall intensified links with the University of Manchester and its Medical School, developing research programmes and new treatments in neurosciences, mental health, and plastic surgery, including cleft lip and palate surgery, as well as providing new specialty services in respiratory medicine, urology and genetics. The hospital also became a lead centre for paediatric intensive care, with the Paediatric Emergency Transfer Service bringing patients from across the North West, and beyond.

The Duchess of York
This hospital had been founded in 1914 by Dr Catherine Chisholm – for women doctors and for the care of babies. It had moved to purpose-built premises in Burnage in 1925 and there continued its work on rickets and prematurity, linking with welfare services and thus pioneering 'community paediatrics', at a time when the (all-male) British Association of Paediatrics took a much narrower view of the field. The hospital diversified in the 1930s, with more surgery, and a strong outpatients department, run by Dr Sylvia Guthrie.

Dr Chisholm had an international reputation and was well regarded at the Medical School. She looked forward to the NHS, but the NHS did not fit the Duchess, partly because it did not discriminate as to the gender of doctors. When Chisholm retired in 1947, her replacement as senior consultant was the new Professor Gaisford, as we have noted. He and his assistant, Dr Holzel, shared many of Dr Chisholm's interests, but perhaps inevitably, Gaisford spent most of his hospital time at Pendlebury, which was much larger. Dr Holzel made the Duchess his main base for his work on milk, but after he was appointed to a chair in 1971, he spent more time at Booth Hall. Though Sylvia Guthrie tried very hard, it was becoming more difficult to justify a small separate hospital in a conurbation that had three other paediatric units as well as facilities in the newer general hospitals. The Duchess doctors, now largely male, became reconciled to a concentration of services; but the Duchess commanded huge public support.

For South Manchester, the problem was solved by moving the Duchess of York service to Withington in 1987 – as the children's unit of the expanding teaching hospital. Many regretted the end of a hospital where women doctors had pioneered the care of babies, and had set national standards for children's nursing, but they could take comfort in the transfer of the name, and in the fact that the Platt report (1959) on children's nursing had broadcast the principles of child care which Harry Platt had learned from Catherine Chisholm and Sylvia Guthrie.

The politics of children's services

In the early 1990s, Booth Hall and the RMCH came under the Salford District Health Authority, which thus controlled most of the region's specialist paediatric beds. As the hospital buildings aged, the future of the children's service became more problematic –– if they were to be replaced, should it be on one site, and if so where? Should children's services be part of all district general hospitals; and if there was to be a specialist hospital for the region, should it be in the central site, or maybe at Pendlebury?

The issue was reviewed in 1988, and the report favoured tertiary services on a single site next to a major adult service. In 1990, the Regional Authority had made clear its preferences for reorganization: Booth Hall would be closed, with its secondary services moving to the North Manchester General; Pendlebury would close, with its secondary services moving to Hope; and a tertiary service would be combined with a secondary service at St. Mary's. A later report suggested that tertiary services could be provided from more than one of the teaching hospitals: Central might develop some, with others at Pendlebury until they could be moved to Hope. All the recommendations were highly controversial and the issue remained live through to the mid 1990s.

When the Central District Health Authority pressed for a merger of Booth Hall and RMCH, Manchester City Council objected and threatened a judicial review. Closing Booth Hall was politically sensitive, especially when the local Labour councillor was leader of the City Council and a potential MP. In 1995, Booth Hall and Pendlebury gained some independence from the Salford and Trafford District Health Authority when they became the Manchester Children's Hospitals NHS Trust, although the District Authority still retained overall control of planning and funding services. When the health authorities were reorganized in 1996, the children question was a priority. The issue involved several hospitals and at least two health authorities, but the new Manchester Health Authority was to lead, with the Regional Office keeping a low profile. The Health Authority was particularly interested in developing community services that would be complemented by secondary services in the hospitals, and a relatively small tertiary centre alongside a leading general hospital. Central Manchester seemed the obvious site, until the chairman and staff of Hope Hospital developed an alternative proposal. Hope had emerged as a strong teaching hospital, and opposed the Medical School's ambition of concentrating tertiary services at the central site.

Nor did the Children's Hospital Trust like the proposal for focussing children's services on the central hospital site; their own chances of remaining independent seemed better in Salford. Furthermore, some of the RMCH and Booth Hall paediatricians preferred a move to Hope, a hospital they saw as well managed and relatively happy compared to the Central Manchester Trust. Such concerns were characteristic of a period when managers were increasingly intervening in the areas that had previously been the domain of doctors. So too was the political use of open meetings – a discussion of the choice between Hope and Central attracted 4-500 people. Towards the end of 1996, management consultants were engaged to assess the relative merits of the proposals from Hope and the MRI. They found both to be acceptable, but the Health Authority preferred the Central site.

The final decision, in favour of Central Manchester, was taken by the Secretary of State in March 1997. After the election of that year, Frank Dobson, the Secretary of State in the new Labour Government, promised that the Children's Hospital could retain its own Trust – a small comfort for those who feared that the peculiar spirit of a children's service would be lost in a large hospital catering chiefly to adults.

The promised outcomes of this decision proved to be long-delayed (building of the new children's hospital did not begin until 2004), but some results followed quickly. Booth Hall began to lose staff, and the intensive-care unit had to close a ward. The Unit was then moved to Pendlebury, so limiting the work of the Booth Hall Burns Unit. And while the teaching hospitals waited for children's services to be concentrated, they continued to develop their secondary level services.

New Labour and the Private Finance Initiative

The New Labour government, which came to power in May 1997, promised considerable extra resources for the NHS – but only after two more years of restraint, and within a framework of yet more reorganization. A further wave of reforms for the NHS was meant to reduce the problem-laden 'internal market', replacing it with a more collaborative model of working, though retaining the division between purchasers and suppliers. Health authorities and fund-holding GPs were to have many of their purchasing and commissioning functions taken over by Primary Care Groups, later Primary Care Trusts – organizations designed to be representative of all the GPs of a district, but also of nurses and other staff. The influence of GPs was in fact diminished, and that of the health authorities increased.

In April 1997, the Central Manchester Trust had received government approval for a £160 million modernization of the Oxford Road site that would see the final removal of the elderly and unsuitable buildings, and their replacement with a series of new structures across the MRI, St. Mary's and the Royal Eye Hospital. The scale of the rebuilding, and the development of a range of new specialist services, necessitated extensive planning and collaboration, combining the efforts of the University, Manchester City Council and Manchester Children's Hospitals Trust, with those of the Central Trust – all within a new framework of 'public-private' partnerships.

New buildings for an historic hospital

Labour had continued the Conservative preference (from 1993) for the funding of major capital projects through Private Finance Initiatives (PFIs) – collaborations with private companies who would build the new hospitals and lease them to the Trust for a generation or so. These arrangements were supposed to provide more efficient building projects, with the companies carrying much of the risk. Critics predicted, and later claimed confirmation, that the public would in fact be left with the risks because no hospital would be allowed to go bust. But PFIs kept hospital capital schemes off the list of national 'public expenditures', and that mattered for the government's spending plans, especially when Labour had promised not to increase public spending during its first two years.

The cost of the projected hospitals on the central site was initially estimated at around £250 million, which meant that a PFI had to be used. The addition of a Children's Hospital meant a large additional expense. In 1998, the two Trusts gained approval for their joint plans for the central site. Now they were to select a consortium to finance and build the new buildings and refurbish old ones. Once this work was completed, the buildings would then be 'leased' to the Trusts over a period of twenty five to thirty years, with regular payments made to cover rent and maintenance.

The companies who were likely to bid for the contract then objected to dealing with two separate Trusts for one site, and the

Regional Office was forced to go to consultation on the possibility of merging the Trusts. The Children's Hospital Trust strongly opposed this move, which involved breaking a written undertaking given by a previous Secretary of State. But to no-one's surprise, the undertaking was broken and the Trusts were merged – as the Central Manchester and Manchester Children's University Hospitals NHS Trust, covering the MRI, Manchester Royal Eye Hospital, St. Mary's Hospital, the University of Manchester Dental Hospital, Booth Hall Children's Hospital, and the Royal Manchester Children's Hospital.

Soon afterwards, a consortium called Catalyst Health Care was selected to build the new hospitals. They also took control of the buildings which were to survive, including the historic frontage. Costs, however, had escalated and were queried by the Primary Care Trusts which would have to pay for the operation of the completed hospitals. Delays followed and some of the plans were scaled down.

A radically new future was taking shape, part of the largest national investment in hospital buildings for at least a century. After c.2000, the NHS began to receive much larger funding – a very welcome move, making up the deficits that had accumulated over 30 years, relative to other European countries. But the Central Manchester project was complex and the context uneasy; the Trust merger was a forced marriage of bodies with very different histories. Furthermore,

Figure 29. The total redevelopment of the Oxford Road site will mark the end for the pavilion style Infirmary with its long wards and even longer connecting corridors.

the new hospital Trust had to respond to a collection of Primary Care Trusts who were just finding their way as newly constituted purchasing authorities; and it was in bed with a business consortium with unprecedented control over the future of the service. These ever-changing complexities well reflected New Labour's attitudes: their substantial injection of funds, their addiction to reorganizations, and their considerable faith in the private sector.

Pasts and futures

Such was the developing context in which the Trust marked two major anniversaries: for 50 years of the NHS in 1998, and for 250 years of the Manchester Royal Infirmary in 2002. To celebrate 1948 was to look back to another Labour government – which had nationalized hospitals to considerable public acclaim and had substantially improved their services. For doctors, this now seemed a golden age. For all their objections at the time, the NHS had brought them secure and salaried employment, and a major voice in the development of the service. In 1998, the salaries were still good, but their influence seemed to be declining.

To celebrate the MRI was to recall the premier medical charity of the Manchester region, which had been essentially autonomous for its first 150 years. For more than a century, it had been closely linked with the University as the sole teaching hospital; and for the first 25 years of the NHS, the doctors of the central hospitals had strongly influenced both their own teaching hospitals, and the district hospitals throughout the region. The university connection, and the cutting-edge developments, however, were now spread across several hospitals, even when the Medical School might have preferred to concentrate more of them on the central site. And though the doctor-manager confrontations of the later 1990s were past, doctors were still adjusting to the 'new public management', not just in the hospitals but also in the new agencies for health-service planning, funding and quality control. The PFI was a further novelty, with consequence yet to be discovered.

For both anniversaries, the MRI opened its doors to the public, and the public responded by flocking to the demonstrations, tours and exhibits. In 1998, past and present staff also helped in the making of a film – part of a series marking fifty years of the NHS, screened by Channel 4. On 18 July 2002, the Mayor of Manchester, Councillor Roy Walters unveiled a blue heritage plaque on Manchester's King Street to mark the site where the house of the Infirmary's founder, Charles White, had once stood. At the other main 250th celebrations held the following day, the TV personality Gordon Burns unveiled a woodcut depicting hospital life through the ages, together with a commemorative plaque. In addition to the on-site exhibitions, the Trust also supported a major internet-based historical celebration of the Infirmary, the production of a CD-ROM containing images and interviews, a series of public outreach events in local schools, and the eventual production of this book.

History is now being remade, and fast; but that dynamism increases the need to learn from the past, including the recent past. Otherwise, in political and managerial worlds with more panaceas than memory, we may continue to spend an awful lot of public resources going round in circles. For organizations, as for patients, a rapid succession of 'restoratives' is rarely good practice, especially where there is little continuity of observation. And for the NHS, as in clinical medicine, evidence of efficacy might be thought a desirable condition for the application of new remedies. In the first quarter-century of the NHS, massive improvements of services were secured with hardly any reorganisations. In the opening years of the new millennium, the majority of NHS staff were longing for some organisational stability, as well as investment – not to remain the same, but to steadily and securely create the facilities which will serve Manchester and its region for decades to come.

Sources
and Additional reading

For the references for chapter one, see Pickstone, *Medicine and Industrial Society* (listed below). The majority of material in chapter 2 of the book came originally from the Minutes, Memos and Annual Reports of the MRI, located in the MRI archive. In addition to producing its own reports, the MRI contributed to the combined United Manchester Hospitals Group Annual Reports series, and these items may be consulted at the Manchester Central Reference Library in the Local Studies Section. Institutional reports of any kind are scarce between the NHS reorganizations of 1974 and the establishment of the new NHS Trust in 1991. For chapters 3–4 we made extensive use of the Manchester University medical students' newspaper, *Mediscope*, and the internal group hospital journals *Telstar* and the later *Central Issues* (all three publications may be consulted at the MRI archive) as well as local newspapers. After 1991, Trust reports provide much more useful and detailed information; and we are also pleased to acknowledge the paper by Pamela Venning, below. Nonetheless, chapters 5–6, like earlier chapters, depended heavily on interviews and personal correspondence with a large number of past and present employees of the Infirmary and other Manchester hospitals, to whom we are very grateful. We have also drawn on, or recommend, the following books and articles.

Barnes, Pamela, *Royal Manchester Children's Hospital "Pendlebury" 1829–1999: Incorporating Booth Hall, Duchess of York and St. Mary's Children's Unit* (Leek, Churnet Valley Books, 1999).

Brockbank, William, *A Portrait of a Hospital, 1752–1948: To Commemorate the Bicentenary of the Royal Infirmary, Manchester* (London, Heinemann, 1952).

Butler, Stella and Pickstone, John V., eds, *Medicine in the Manchester Region, John Rylands Library Bulletin*, vol. 87, November 2007 (dated 2005).

Calnan, James, *The Hammersmith Hospital: The First Fifty Years of the Royal Postgraduate School at the Hammersmith Hospital, 1935–1985* (Lancaster, MTP Press, 1985).

Elwood, Willis, and Tuxford, Félicité, eds, *Some Manchester Doctors: A Biographical Collection to Mark the 150th Anniversary of the Manchester Medical Society, 1834–1984* (Manchester Medical Society by Manchester University Press, 1984).

Ham, C, *Health Policy in Britain: The Politics and Organization of the National Health Service*, 5th edition (Basingstoke, Palgrave, 2004).

Harrison, S, *Managing the National Health Service in the 1980s; Policy Making on the Hoof?* (Aldershot, Avebury, 1994)

Heaman, Elsbeth, *St. Mary's: The History of a London Teaching Hospital* (Liverpool, Liverpool University Press, 2003).

Jones, Emma L, and Pickstone, John V, *The Quest for Public Health in Manchester. The industrial city, the NHS and the recent history* (published by the Manchester Primary Care Trust in association with the Centre for the History of Science, Technology and Medicine, University of Manchester, 2008. Distributed by Carnegie Publishing, 01524 840111 www.carnegiepublishing.com).

Klein, Rudolf, *The New Politics of the NHS. From Creation to Reinvention*, (Fifth edition: Oxford, Radcliffe, 2006).

Lawrence, Christopher, 'Clinical Research', in John Krige and Dominic Pestre, eds, *Science in the Twentieth Century* (Amsterdam, Harwood, 1997), 439–459.

McLachlan, Gordon, *A History of the Nuffield Provincial Hospitals Trust 1940–1990* (London, Nuffield Provincial Hospitals Trust, 1992).

Magnello, Eileen, *A Centenary History of the Christie Hospital Manchester* (Manchester, Christie Hospital NHS Trust, 2001).

Pickstone, John V., *Medicine and Industrial Society: A History of Hospital Development of Manchester and its Region, 1752–1946* (Manchester, Manchester University Press, 1985).

Pickstone, John V., 'Medicine, Natural History and Owens College', and 'Medicine, Nursing and the Life Sciences, 1903–2000', in Brian Pullan ed., *The University of Manchester, an Illustrated History* (London, Third Millennium Press, 2007).

Pickstone, John V., 'Science and Technology in Manchester: An Introduction to the History', in John V. Pickstone, ed., *Science and Technology in the North West, Manchester Regional History Review*, vol. 18 (June 2007), 1–18.

Rivett, Geoffrey, *From Cradle to the Grave: Fifty Years of the NHS* (London, Kings Fund, 1998).

Valier, Helen K., 'The Politics of Scientific Medicine in Manchester, c.1900–1960,' PhD thesis, University of Manchester, 2002.

Valier, Helen K., 'The Manchester Royal Infirmary, 1945–1997: A

Microcosm of the NHS', *Bulletin of the John Rylands University Library*, *Vol 87, number 1*, November 2007 (2005), 167–92.

Venning, Pamela, *Analysing Strategic Change in Greater Manchester* (a paper from the Manchester (University) Centre for Health Care Management, nd, c. 2002)

Waddington, Keir, *Medical Education at St. Bartholomew's Hospital, 1123–1995* (Woodbridge, Boydell, 2003).

Wade, Lesley and Hallett, Christine, 'The Dynamic City: Recruitment to Nursing in early 20th Century Manchester', *Nurse Education Today*, 23 (2003), 370–9.

Webster, Charles, *The Health Services since the War. Volume 1: Problems of health care. The National Health Service before 1957* (London, HMSO, 1988); *Volume 2: Government and health care. The British National Health Service, 1958–1979* (London, HMSO, 1996).

Webster, Charles, *The National Health Service: a Political History* (Second edition: Oxford, Oxford University Press, 2002).

Wilson, Duncan, *Reconfiguring Biological Sciences in the Late Twentieth Century. A Study of the University of Manchester* (published by the Faculty of Life Sciences, University of Manchester, in association with the Centre for the History of Science, Technology and Medicine, University of Manchester, 2008)

Index

Poor Law, 2, 4, 15–16, 21
Portrait of a Hospital, A, ix, 38
Powell, Enoch, 40, 46
Private Patients' Home (PPH),
    18–19, 21–22, 64, 91
problem-based approach, 88–89
Project 2000, 72–73
psychiatry, 3, 24, 28, 33, 42, 47, 50,
    63, 80, 83, 86, 95, 99–100, 102–103
Public Health Act (1848), 4

Quarter Century Club, 66–67

Radford, Thomas, 6
Ramsden, Richard, 81
Rawnsley Day Hospital, 83
Regional Burns Unit, 102, 105
renal medicine and services, 33–34,
    54–56, 80–81, 92, 95–96, 98, 101,
    103
rheumatism, 33–36, 41, 54
Robert Barnes Medical Unit, 80
Roberton, John, 6
Roberts, Frances, 66, 70–71
Roberts, Lloyd, 6
Roe, Humphrey, 15
Roscoe, Henry, 9
Rothschild Report on Medical Research,
    54
Royal Eye Hospital. *See* Manchester
    Royal Eye Hospital
Royal Manchester Children's
    Hospital, 1, 7–8, 20, 28, 32, 94–
    95, 100–105, 107
royal visits, 42, 85, 92–93

Salford Royal Hospital, 5, 16, 42, 99
Salford Teaching Hospital Group, 40
Salmon Report, The, 46
Samelson, Adolph, 12
Sellors, Sir Thomas Holmes, 55
Shaw, Walter Fletcher, 16
Skinner, Colin, 22
Somerville, Margaret, 12
Southern Hospital, 12
Sparshott, Margaret, 10–11, 58

Spens Report, The, 27
St. Luke's Clinic, 32, 60
St. Mary's Hospital, 1, 4, 6, 12,
    14–15, 22–24, 32, 42–44, 60, 64,
    77–78, 84–85, 90, 95, 106–107
Stopes, Marie, 15
Stopford, Lord John, 14, 16, 20, 26,
    29–33, 35, 49
Stott, W. Barton, 5
Structural Engineers Report (1977),
    63
Super, Maurice, 101

Telstar, 46–48, 61
Tomlinson, Stephen, 68–69, 73
tuberculosis, 14–16, 32, 101
Turnberg, Leslie, 50
Turner, Sir Samuel, 15, 17

United Manchester Hospitals
    (UMH), 1, 20, 22, 24, 27–29,
    36–38, 40–44, 46–49, 54–56,
    60–61, 66
University of Manchester, ix, 17, 20,
    29–36, 40, 49–53, 61, 69, 74–75,
    88–90, 95, 97, 99–100, 103, 106,
    109
University Research Centre for the
    Study of Chronic Rheumatism,
    33–36

Walters, Roy, 109
Warrell, David, 86
*Welfare of Sick Children in Hospitals,
    The*, 102
Wellcome Trust, The, 41, 90
Wellings, Sylvia, 46–47
White, Charles, 3, 4, 109
Whitehead, James, 7
Whitworth, Joseph, 10
Whitworth, Linda, 56
Wilkinson, John, 33
Wilson, Donald, 96
Wilson, Elizabeth, 48
Wilson, William James, 5
Windsor, Thomas, 5